Mis

ADOLPHE RETTÉ (1863-1930) was on the editorial staff of *La Vogue*, and published his first collection of poems, *Cloches en la nuit*, in 1889. That was followed by the remarkable *Thulé des Brumes* (Bibliothèque Artistique et Littéraire, 1891), a portmanteau of dream-like prose poems. He experienced something of an ideological conversion in 1893 when he became a committed anarchist and gave his allegiance to an esthetic theory that preached the necessity of a return to nature and a celebration of everyday life. In 1906 he underwent another conversion, this time to Catholicism, and his subsequent literary work was doctrinaire.

BRIAN STABLEFORD has been publishing fiction and non-fiction for fifty years. His fiction includes an eighteen-volume series of "tales of the biotech revolution" and a series of half a dozen metaphysical fantasies set in Paris in the 1840s, featuring Edgar Poe's Auguste Dupin. His most recent non-fiction projects are *New Atlantis: A Narrative History of British Scientific Romance* (Wildside Press, 2016) and *The Plurality of Imaginary Worlds: The Evolution of French* roman scientifique (Black Coat Press, 2016); in association with the latter he has translated approximately a hundred and fifty volumes of texts not previously available in English, similarly issued by Black Coat Press.

Adolphe Retté

Misty Thule

Translated and with an Introduction by
Brian Stableford

THIS IS A SNUGGLY BOOK

ISBN: 978-1-943813-70-4

CONTENTS

INTRODUCTION

THULÉ DES BRUMES by Adolphe Retté, here translated as *Misty Thule*, was first published in Paris by Bibliothèque Artistique et Littéraire in 1891; excerpts had previously been published in the Belgian periodical *La Wallonie* in 1890. It was the author's second book, following the poetry collection *Cloches en la nuit* [Bells in the Night] (1889). It became one of the key documents of the Symbolist Movement, one of the most extreme illustrations of the philosophy of that Movement, based on Stéphane Mallarmé dictum that the writer ought to record, in symbolic terms, the impressions made by objects and events rather than the objects and events themselves. Mallarmé also urged the proponents of his theory to test the limits of the imagination, and *Thulé des Brumes* does that too.

The Symbolist Movement's detractors claimed that the obliquity of the method, coupled with a fascination with dreams, visions and altered states of consciousness, often produced confusion, incoherence and incomprehensibility, and that is a charge to which Adolphe Retté was certainly not immune during the phase of his career in which he produced *Thulé des Brumes*. The Movement's practitioners and defenders, however, answered with the claim that any attempt to pin down the current of conscious experience by means of precise description and rational interpretation is a kind of falsification, because actual experience really is disorderly and confused, and frequently dissolves into incoherence, always retaining a margin of incomprehensibility.

There are few volumes that reflect that notion of literary reportage more fully than *Thulé des Brumes*, and perhaps none that go quite as far in breaking down the ordering systems conventionally applied to that reportage, deliberately breaching the usually-imposed boundaries of poetry and prose, sensation and fantasy, stories and chapters, syntax and punctuation. That fracturing is sufficiently extreme in this instance to qualify the work as Surrealism *avant la lettre*, reaching toward an immediacy of raw representation that attempts to gag the censor of rationalization and liberate the anarchic thrust of the unconscious as a hidden participant in the processes of perception and mental response.

Thulé des Brumes is perhaps most easily considered as a collection of poems in prose, in the tradition of Charles Baudelaire's unfinished *Spleen de Paris*, but it is by no means a collection of disparate elements; it is possessed not only of forceful connecting threads but also an enclosing frame, which might even invite its consideration as an *avant-garde* novel. Like Joris-Karl Huysmans, who categorized the prose poem as "the osmazome of literature," Retté found it an ideal form for attempting to capture the fleeting impressions whose sum, reflectively tabulated and smoothed, constitutes the fabric of everyday life, but there is nothing haphazard about the way that Retté employs it; there is a sequence in his assembly, which eventually comes to comprise a sum of sorts, albeit one that remains jagged, uncondensed into a continuous narrative of the kind that literary endeavor has long encouraged us to make of our lives.

In order to appreciate *Thulé de Brumes* fully it is necessary to have some idea of how it fit into the contexts of the author's life and career. Adolphe Retté was born in 1863 and initially embarked on a military career in 1881, serving in the army until 1887 before deciding to devote himself to literature instead. In 1888 he married his cousin, Marie Renoz, but the honeymoon period of the marriage was short-lived; it soon became turbulent, and the couple separated some time before Marie's death in 1890. *Thulé des Brumes* was written in the aftermath of the personal catastrophe in question. The author dates the composition of the work between October 1889 and January 1891, and represents it as the chronicle of a single year: essentially, the year after his separation from his wife. The fact of Marie's death while the text was in production is only mentioned occasionally, and obliquely—as, for instance, when the Pauper tells Juliet's fortune—as if it were considered almost irrelevant, but it would be surprising if the occurrence had not had a marked effect upon progress of the author's maudlin and rancorous feelings. It was not, however, the cause of those feelings, and it is the death of the marriage, not the death of the wife, to which the text is principally a reaction.

The text declares frankly that part of the reaction in question involved heavy drinking, and many of the hallucinations recorded in its fragments are doubtless alcohol induced. Some of the pieces do give the impression of having being written while drunk or hung over, but the great majority are surely the product of bitter sober reflection, possessed of a kind of incoherency that is quite conscious and controlled, albeit emotionally raw and sometimes frankly agonized.

"Thule" is an inherently symbolic location, being used by Classical and Medieval geographers—usually in the phrase Ultima Thule—to signify the world's most northerly landmass, usually conceived as an island, belonging more to the realm of legend than reality because of its practical inaccessibility. Retté's notion of it is essentially fantastic, located in the unconscious mind; it is, for him, the source of dreams and Poetry, the wellspring of literary creativity. The attempts of his narrative alter ego, the Pauper, to reach it therefore constitute a journey in inner space, an exercise in deep-psyche diving.

The Pauper represents the quest, naturally, as an attempt to escape from unbearable reality, no matter what the cost, accepting the inevitable burden of darkness and freezing fog—but the destination only figures in the endeavor as a kind of magnetic north pole, whose inaccessibility is immaterial. Even in reality, proverbial wisdom assures us, it is better to travel hopefully than to arrive, and in literary endeavor it is also better to travel hopelessly, because it is the travel—the artistic endeavor—that matters, rather than the hope.

Retté was by no means alone among the Symbolists in following in the footsteps of Robert Burton in attempting to produce an anatomy of his melancholy, and in the process of that analysis to oppose it—not necessarily to cure it, but at least to keep it at bay and parry its most mortal thrusts. Nor was he alone in concluding his work with a report of his progress and a mental health-check of sorts, and he was certainly not alone in then finding that the prescription had to be repeated. Where he was unusual, however, is that his repeat prescriptions varied very markedly. Although he continued writing until the end of his life—he died in 1930—he never wrote another book resembling *Thulé des Brumes*, his subsequent exercises in Symbolism burning other, less smoky, fuel.

In the mid-1890s Retté committed himself ardently to the political cause of Anarchism, and much of his work for the next decade was devoted to the active promotion of that philosophy. That affiliation colored his memoir of the Symbolist Movement, *Le Symbolisme, anecdotes et souvenirs* (1903), but the coloration does not detract from its importance as a historical document. In 1906, however, he underwent another similarly-wholehearted conversion, to devout Catholicism—his mother was a Catholic but his father was not; he had been brought up with liberal views, so it was not a reversion—and the final phase of his literary career, was devoted almost entirely to doctrinaire writing. It is, of course, easy to make judgments with the aid of hindsight, but readers of *Thulé des Brumes*, even at the time of its first publication, could not have had overmuch difficulty in identifying the seeds of those future conversions, or at least in recognizing that it was the work of a man ever likely to grasp at seemingly-promising existential straws whenever he became alarmed by the prospect of drowning in woe.

That is not to criticize the author or the book in any way; indeed, it is a compliment to an unusual heroic determination, remarkably flexible in its ingenuity. Retté's Thule was always going to prove ungraspable, mist being even less likely to aid flotation than straw, but the strength and glory of the work are in the act of reaching out with a clutching hand. That, both the author and the book did, with force, with style, and with effect. Although Retté repudiated the book in later life, on religious grounds, and had turned against Mallarmé and his philosophy even before then, on political grounds, *Thulé des Brumes* remains the most remarkable work that he produced—and, indeed, one of the most remarkable that anyone produced under the aegis of Symbolism.

This translation was made from the copy of the 1891 edition reproduced on the Bibliothèque Nationale's *gallica* website.

—Brian Stableford

Misty Thule

PREFACE

"*THE REALITIES of the world affected me as visions, and as visions only, while the wild ideas of lands of dreams became, in turn, not the material of my everyday existence but in very deed that existence utterly and solely in itself . . .*"

Who said that? Egaeus the Metaphysician.[1]

For certain complex souls of these hostile times, there are days when life becomes so hostile, the ambience so asphyxiating, that they take refuge recklessly in dreams. Then—sometimes for months on end—the soul lives an abnormal and grandiose existence; ideas are exasperated and deformed; sentiments take on a formidable intensity; sensations are impregnated with voluptuous suffering; the Self abandons its divine principle and the will is no longer anything but a stormy Ocean on which mad ships are tossed.

If, during such a period—the glory of the Demon—Fatality determines that an obsession takes possession of

---

1 The quotation is from Edgar Poe's "Berenice," an archetypal study of morbid obsession, of which Egaeus [meaning, approximately, "out of the library"] is the protagonist.

15

a soul thus displaced from its orbit; if, for example, the passionate desire for a feminine Appearance implants itself there and dominates it to the point of *incarnating* the obsession, a solitary intoxication bursts forth that almost goes as far as dementia. But the Self cherishes its folly; in order to multiply it tenfold and perpetuate it, it penetrates into the luminous and criminal empire that the stimulants open to it; it forgets itself there and *does not want to be cured*. It requires a violent hazard—some might say a miracle—for the soul to recover its equilibrium and be saved.

Such is the meaning of this book. Some might condemn it, especially because of the forbidden joys that enfever it and the special sensuality that it contains. Others might love it for its sad Artistry and because it is the memoir of a dream.

PROLOGUE

*S*O *pale, like the sad wall of a monastery*
Bleeding from a sweet anxiety that would do better to
                                                    [shut up,
    Lady of Autumn with the faded hands
    My soul floats in the twilight.

Sobs of a fabulous wave, ephemeral clouds.
Golden sky, vibrant silks of enervated harps;
    Is it the Euphrates in which you will slake the thirst
        Of my poor enamored dream?

"I know not . . . I would like to drink from the very breeze
A little of the fresh forgetfulness that sleeps in the branches;
Or, virginal first light, hope of future dawns,
Kneel at the far-distant threshold of a new church!

And yet, and yet, O proud solitude,
Amid your dead perfumes and the frisson of evenings,
I see again the slow hymn of pale suns, prelude
    To a chorus wept by our black archangels,
Prophets of the Night that your silence eludes.

O indecisive mirage that must not fade
O chilly charm of slender foliage—
It is the fainting lute of Saint Cecilia . . .

But what gesture violates my docile weakness?
Here is laughing Circe and her opiate philter:
I drink . . . I am the very strong and very subtle god—
And the Anxiety that has wounded me limps away.

O sidereal poison in which the Dream fulgurates,
     Unique throne: Illusion!
A flock of golden birds bursts forth, which lift me
Toward a park ablaze with red florescence.

Adieu wingless life and gray reason:
The clouds have fled where my prison was
     —Youth, I know your fountain!—
And, saved from the obscure crowd that trudges,
I shall finally pluck those distant stars."

NOCTURNAL SMOKE

There are crepuscular things
Visions of the end of the night . . .
PAUL VERLAINE.[1]

---

1 The lines are from the "Prologue" to the Naguère section of the
collection *Jadis et Naguère* (1891).

※

MERCIFUL DARKNESS, Charity of innocent eyes from whose golden lashes distant tears filter palely, the Night spreads its pacifying silence in waves over the agitated slumber of the city. The winged fingers of subtle spirits stir the high-pitched strings of delicate harps; an unusual epithalamium floats for the wedding of a soul with the Mystery.

Wellspring of all graces—among the lilies of recollection: serene water, coveted fluid gem in which the barbarities of Living are drowned; bright sobbing river furrowed by luminous gondolas—the murmurous mourning of memorial viols lulls there the ennui of a deformed prince in hiding—mirror of melancholy and forgetfulness offering the blue and wintry silks of lunar solitudes—after so many burning stages—to the fatigue of a pilgrimage to the basilica of Nothingness; forests of Gulistan, cool shadows that enshroud you, sick soul that was corroded only yesterday by the salts of the Desolate Sea—the good maternal Night caresses the fragile infancy of the Dream—oh, let it never survive the furtive gleam of a first light that might perhaps reveal it as an abortion—

the holy starry Night lights candles for the mass of the Ideal—oh, let the brutal fanfares of the sun never surge forth from the quotidian horizon. Let me be in that smiling Night, let the velvet charm of that mystic Night descend into me—and you will not have me any longer, monstrous Life, famished nightmare whose mouths lie in wait for me . . .

Toward the empire of shadows, forever secluded from the tranquil blue of Saturnine days—far from the gaze of a bored woman—(serenity still young, in demi-tints, of an autumn whose terminus I do not want to know, and even whether it must expire more gravely when the flowers of snow fall outside on soon violated flower-beds, when the widows are starred with serpentine gems—winter kept at bay, but nevertheless close at hand, by that frail prismatic barrier and frost) the Foundation awaits, its thought wandering over the jewels of adventure: not the cold kiss of a jade bracelet nor the northern amber of a necklace, but little golden bells, the passage of tame hippogriffs in the utmost depths of the silks of my soul, the nacre of a palace under the ocean, a slender viol, also, dormant with the rhythms that will sing one evening, softly, to-ward Her—an evening when the rusty bells will lose their clappers, when, for the glory of her light breasts, the sole essential of my dreams will blossom.

Ahead, the ice-sheets launch needles of turquoise and emerald into a sky of dead steel—the excessively correct rectilinear ice-sheets that circle the horizon, a line incurved toward a necessarily flat pole. Behind, as far as the eye can see, the sparse earth is a whiteness of irremediable plains, awaiting the Arctic spring. But what will grow there?

If the sun is lukewarm, meager lichens and sad pink heather, the one who was dreaming just now—and her pale blue eyes—will perhaps pass by next year; we will offer her a poor bouquet.

Today, though, who inhabits that solitude?

Standing on a block of ice—a bleak pedestal!—a polar bear sways, a learned bear that has seen the cities of the South; it has been beaten with cudgels there, but it had learned a few things; if fact, it grunts: "Gnothi seauton."[1]

An aged seal gorged on fish, slumped on the edge of a crevasse, sniggers at it.

The clown—whose butterfly had burned its wings in so many chandeliers—said to his friend: "If you think it is sufficient for me to have woven the cloth of my soul with stars, if you imagine that bearing in perpetuity the train of that Queen of Sheba, Illusion, is a joy for me—it is true that in other circumstances I have extended to

1 "Know thyself": a Greek aphorism reportedly inscribed in the forecourt of the Temple of Apollo at Delphi, a key element in the philosophy of Socrates, Plato and Epicurus.

Fantasy the dream circles in which I hoped it would remain a prisoner, but it fell back, svelte, on to the back of our indefatigable black horse (I think it's a demon) and galloped further on—if, finally, you haven't yet perceived the precious stones that I spit out among such toads— and they aren't paste, you can verify that—empty that glass in which liquid mourning is stagnating and tell me about the Tribocci:[1] then we might resemble everyone else."

But the friend broke his glass on the floorboards and kept silent, for, deep down, he understood very well.

They walk stiffly in the friezes of the palace of Xerxes, robes of gold and faces of ebony, grave and age-old, in accordance with the majesty they protect: the archers.

Meanwhile, below them, a very small gray palace is heaped; there is no one at the porticoes; there will never be anyone again.

People pass by who look at those archers; take it for granted that they are slightly afraid, and that it annoys them.

Reassure yourselves, people, they are prisoners in a cage of glass, their quivers are empty and *they* are silent for eternity.

1 The Tribocci were a Germanic people encountered by Julius Caesar during the Gallic Wars, living in a region that embraces much of modern Alsace.

The baying of dog packs echoes through the forest. In the clearings that the martial sun dapples with new gold, in the thickets where ponds open a mossy eye, the hunting horn becomes hoarse.

So does an ephebe hunting in the afternoon; the shadows lengthen, the jeers of crows accompany him and the hamadryad—who has been an arch-centenarian for centuries—sings to him: "You won't catch it." His horse gallops.

The forest bleeds twilight; the weary horse has slowed to a walk; the horn is broken and the aureole of the divine hunter is hanging, torn, from the low branches.

Now the Night is rising; the dogs fall silent and lie down, curled up. Will the beasts be caught, by chance? The horse is dead.

Lightened, finally—how many years has that hunt lasted?—an old hunter advances and looks. There is nothing, nothing but the moonlight, entirely alone, spreading shrouds on the ground.

There was a day—a long time ago . . .

The fragile adolescent girl, to be married tomorrow, perhaps to an ageless magician, descends the sonorous steps toward the waves—languid mauve, jonquil kisses, camellia petals smitten with a tremor like the satins that adorn her, and the sidereal mystery of a talisman given by a friendly fay: the convex tumultuous crown of her hair—and regrets the excessively brief descent while the harps of fleeting Oceanides serenade her, like fine flocks of seagulls, in soft arpeggios over the sea. And the wind drums the cliffs like a madman.

Land the funeral gondola, light the torches, in order that that lover, henceforth asleep, will float all alone, since no one will pass over her frail finger the ring that the Devil will keep from her.

She is a virgin Poetry (but no longer for me) soon to venture over the Ocean (give her a palm); in order that, to safeguard her, she has out there in her homeland, Misty Thule, a prayer on the pure lips of her sisters, dead for having been cloistered (personally, I still have her mystic flower: shut up, waves) or even (there are pirates on the sea) that she has some strange realm—or even that the maternal swans of Artemis might carry her to the Moon; myself, I was only a church widowed of the holy ciborium, she an excessively proud silver bell.

They are the good poets, sick of a Psyche, who prowl black puddles and splash one another with dirty water and variegated rhymes.

One late autumn, Arachne extends her pluvious web over the city, and the silk of viscous fogs everywhere; the bells cough out the hours at length; somber tintinnabulations, impalpable bats, fly through the streets and the squares; gutters sign a prophecy; one would think it a confused Atlantis.

Here the tavern invites; Sancho Panza is asleep at the counter; he sells the helmet of Mambrino and keeps the soul of Don Quixote captive in the drawer with the copper coins—that night of neuralgia, in recollections, in empty compromises and things that are resuscitated.

Eternal Mounis[1] haloed with pale vapor, they are two poets. And while for them, burned topazes dance on the table, one of them, discordant, says: "My shoes have holes."

And the other: "Wet feet make warm brains."

And then they drink and smoke without saying anything more; Sancho, in a bad mood at the counter, the tavern torpid and the street outside; Arachne darts her long cold feet there, but does not catch anyone; the gutters bleed in A minor; a consumptive weathervane beats time. In a moment one will be—gray and red Palestine is rising—the sultan Suleiman-ben-Daoud memorizing the *Song of Songs* because of a distant Shulamite and setting out the glorious carpet of his soul for the coming of Balkis—she will not come; the other contemplates the flow of the violet Ganges where the great pachyderms come to drink at dawn; the fraternal bamboos lean over and caress his pine with their down, and piously he adores, the issue of his navel, forever Arya, the blue lotus that contains the Trimurti—but they are only the fumes of alcohol and tobacco.

In a corner, councilor Krespel[2] torments his shrill violin; the ineluctable twilights reign, and now, suddenly, the bleak wisterias of unconscious cenotaphs flourish and

---

1 Retté routinely calls the Buddha Cakya-Mouni, as many French sources do.
2 In E. T. A. Hoffmann's story "Rat Krespel" (1819; tr. as "Councillor Krespel" and "The Cremona Violin").

wrap around their numb thighs, growing all the way to their foreheads.

Finally—hosanna!—the crystal towers of future Mont Salvats rise into the misty air.

In ecstasy beneath the tree of life, I impregnate myself with the floral torments stimulated by the breezes of the terrestrial paradise, and I listen to the distant clinking of the golden chain that shackles the puerile ankles of Salammbô.

The branches of the tree sway; their rustle, a sistrum agitated for a barbaric celebration. There are fruits among the branches, beautiful vermilion fruits, but I do not pick them; my old cousin the Serpent, hidden in the branches, recommends me not to touch them.

However, some are lying on the grass; ripe, the wind has detached them. What if I were to taste that one . . . ?

Oh, the frightful bitterness!

A cold sweat falls from the glaucous foliage of the tree; *for the first time*, a cloud hides the sun; the birds observe with a whistle, mockingly; the breeze disperses the reek of a cadaver and weeps orphan affections. The Serpent cries: "I told you so!" and Salammbô has broken her golden chain.

Tree of life and fruits of death.

A profane lake, which was once sacred—the herdsmen of the high plateaux have mirrored their genius, the fame of soma, therein, as the primitive dawn unfolds its gonfalons—a lake in which the phantom of a grave midnight is eternalized and presides over the dances of the fog, lace and muslin modulated harmoniously toward the classic cliff of a girdle of willows and poplars: the willows in plumes of some tomb, the poplars dolorous lyres amid the wind, and sad candles; wan laughter in the chrysoprase of the sky; that is the moon. Wavelets pursue one another in accordance with some feeble current and scarcely succeed in stirring the pride of nymphea flowers, those delicate individuals strutting because of their necklaces, and which are, however, so defunct. Indefatigably, in that midnight devoid of tomorrow, the genteel croaking of a frog emphasizes the silence—the broad silence fallen upon the water, the willows, the poplars, and able to laugh again at the dream of the night.

The legendary history that the frog is vibrating, the undulating anxiety expanded in the sleepy night, voices whispering distantly: so much silence pampers the lake of the ancestors until the day of sunlight and redemption when the sphinx strangled somewhere under the trees tears its sound of ivy and cries a phrase desired by all:

"The poplars are weeping in the wind and the willows."

On that day—it sometimes shines—joy thunders from virile organs, the loud golden clamor of the buccinas of glory radiates for a triumph, and the rejuvenated surge of the Anadyomene of the lake propagates agile myths; she waves the fiery standard of her hair and flies, her eyes bewildered, toward the slow majesty of an Olympus out there in the depths of the ages. You will shine on the day of sunlight and redemption!

(It is a midnight of Youth.) Afterwards, another day dies; it is no longer anything but lame lines staining the paper; in the hypogea where the smoke is trailing, someone is seeking his soul and cannot find it; for a long time yet it will be drowned in the slothful lake.

The summer night ablaze with stars fills her eyes—but fortunately, she knows nothing about it. That charm! How different it is from that of other eyes, cold darknesses deeply unconscious, in which accursed woods are dormant; and the vanity of the body she does not have— yes, that charm.

Others pretend to be unaware of their beauty, or rather let fall in that regard: "You find me beautiful? That's all the same to me; I know it better than you do."

But that tranquil charm of her eyes, entirely hers, the nocturnal summer of her eyes; the charm, I tell you . . .

Expand the precarious prettiness of fans; slowly, let them amuse sticky-eyed Insomnia; quickly, let them cloud with brief rainbows the vapors of your shrill aromatics—O city of artifices!

Fans, in the darkness, are bouquets of pale fire, the snow of lunar cascades over a clump of asphodels, noble garlands of Panathenaeas.

A mocking procession hurtles pell-mell with the frantic course of clouds, and throws Her milky pearls from above. She does not pick them up, She knows that in reality they are balls of painted glass. For myself, on certain evenings I collect them, but I throw them away sooner or later and come to kneel are her feet, near the hearth powdered with cold ash. There—the wind is singing in the chimneys—I have once again, for a long time, a luminous dream of boats bobbling in the blue calm of her eyes and, the window ajar, the caress swells the fresh fans that entice Insomnia sagely.

Lindens in flower embalm that night.

Let the flames of the pyre loom up in the shadow; the crimson of youth, that excessively narrow diadem, the blunted sword, and those manuscripts of the Kabbalah that teach no one anything, since we divined their doctrine in childhood, let them be burned—also that tress of multicolored hair.

Palely blue eyes invite me to silence; the Maia on the edge of the sea has smiled at me; I am going to sleep between her breasts.

Undoubtedly, it would be better to live. "Life is action, and action is joy," says one philosophy. But a pale face—so fortunately pale—in a nimbus of etiolating lilies, in a voice through which flocks of golden cherubim pass, sings to me: "Happiness is made with dreams."

I nod in approval—and then, and then, my life, mine, is the frail plant of a dream whose essential growth I love to survey. I do not admit that "things" distract me from that care; and, if it is absolutely necessary to incur the fatigue of an effort, I prefer that mine be devoted to smoothing unreal flowers—thus, vaguely, with no other goal than infiltrating a little of their pollen all the way to my heart.

Meanwhile, a Pauper surges forth, humble and arrogant at the same time, summoned to appear before a conclave of necromancers. Oh, the dull red gazes darted at that pitiful wretch, and how his aureole—recuperated from adventures—offends their diabolical reality.

The president has collected the opinions: there is unanimity (Oh, those maleficent individuals, the true afternoon of the dog days of the soul) the sentence is pronounced: "It is necessary that the Pauper undergo proofs; let us hope that he will break his neck therein."

And the Pauper, passably insouciant, unsuspecting, goes toward the pitfalls . . .

But the proofs begin, immediately, with dark eyes.

I collect the wings of Chimeras. Already, a certain num-ber—coldly detached—are falling into dust between the leaves of many albums hidden in the depths of a solid cupboard more than a little worm-eaten—a family heirloom of which I am proud; it has been subjected to so many assaults!

But one last Chimera, pursued for a long time, once seized me in its bronze claws, just as I was about to vanquish it, and carried me away to a black double star then unknown to the sky of my dreams. It took me away so profoundly that your earth, messieurs, is no more to me than an ashy glow. That is why you might hear rather poorly the phrases that I am striving to proffer for your instruction. Do not hold it against me; I am so far away from you, and so bewildered because of the somber marvels that flourish in that black double star.

A stubborn immanence, in spite of everything and through everything, this rage of thought! "No, you shall not be the desired brute," someone says, "Whatever your ennui, you will still grab your Self by the hair to drag it into the cold broad daylight of consciousness, and you will feed on the capering absurdities of your petulant fundamental soul—and you will think."

And I cry, joyfully: "Good, good, a time will surely come when the two of us will reach the most immaculate summits of Metaphysics. In the meantime, let us break a few of the facets of the microcosm in order to study what there is in the heart. And isn't that the wisest thing, tell me, my consciousness (since it's you that I'm invoking) instead of troubling by our austere attitude the light bearded fauns of the turbulent lees braying within us?"

33

And my very judicious consciousness responds to me (I believe that it has definitely lost all moral sense): "I would really like to rediscover the ass's head that Bottom had, which we could put on; doubtless we could then please ourselves, for one night at least, with a few caprices of Titania; that would still be a satisfaction given to our folly—and we would put off by as much the scarcely enviable day when we will hatch out the only Metaphysics in the grottoes of ice."

"My consciousness, you astonish me a little . . . not too much . . ."

Afterwards, crouching before the joyful fire—Cakya-Mouni, I once studied your attitudes—I juggle recklessly with precious balls of blue, green, pink and jet: my ideas. Each one, in colliding with the black marble ceiling where silver goats run, vibrates and resonates as broadly as plainsong; a hundred lyrical cathedrals roaring with swirling increase and triumphant rose-windows—an empyrean of celebrations in explosions of such furious flowers; on the altar, the Holy Sacrament spins like a crazy windmill of light . . .

Oh! This time, I have thrown my ideas with such force that they traverse the ceiling and fly away, whistling—bolides amid the tenebrous Unconscious, my unique sky. The *real* world will never see them again. Cheered up by that spectacle, the owl of Pallas, perched on the clock, weeps with laughter. In order to close this little intimate fête worthily, what if I were to gouge out its large empty eyes?

However, it is necessary to distract oneself: to that effect, a few more days go by.

You see, I am lying in the young grass on the edge of this stream, which quivers with gentle ripples. How warm and blue and pigeon-throated it is out there toward the defile where the stream hides; the wavelets splash, burnished silver hump-backed with spangles; one might think it were the laughter of a tickled cat—and I like that stupid song.

So, idle, my face swept in the trellis like the peak of some capricious cap by the fine thongs of a willow, I am gladly a god in repose, satisfied with the landscape created and above all with having evoked the fresh scents with which he finishes off his dream.

The sky, furrowed by opulent blonde clouds that rear up, is entirely in accordance with my ultrahuman nonchalance. Upstream—my everyday intelligence—is a bridge where the noises of hilarious people and nicely painted carriages are entangled; downstream—tomorrow's soul— the fluid satins of the mists float over the defile, starry and perfumed by drooping jasmines, and from which comes, perhaps, the growl of a cataract sparkling with foam, the cadavers of giants that are to be immolated later—in the future. In the meantime, they are building illusory Babels.

And the god picks blades of grass and throws them to whirl in the splashing water—and the god goes to sleep, in the consciousness of his strength.

✳

Concentric parks of undulating shadow, curling and then uncurling, infinitely, their filigree foliage; prosperous black ostrich-feathers, which, teased by the Etesian breeze, rain little flakes on to the dust of blue pathways; a bunch of tulips with, here and there, a gladiolus, prisms play under the mysteries of the diffuse light of an eclipse. In a basin, frosted with the congealed tears of last year's stars, water as somber as remorse, dreams and deforms within itself the reflection of a pale eyeless face.

Whence comes that face, since no one has ever mirrored themselves herein?

A very old Prince, although so young, on an organ installed in the peristyle of a ruined temple, plays tunes that madden the sylphs of his soul and all the winds, and are inflated, inflated in the golden night, and to which, everywhere, responds the flute of the Great Pan.

Promenades along the yellow inertia of canals, stations eternalized in a viscous fog torn by the hoarse cries of maneuvering locomotives—counting the blows of the pickax of a workman whose physiognomy, humble and rascally at the same time, is observing the grimaces of an ape attached there by an acrobat getting drunk in the tavern on the corner. Too simple, those grimaces; in us (atavism and selection, what else!) it is a much more complex game—as witness the schema of avarice and cunning inscribed by the wrinkles of the dirty face of my hostess as soon as it is a matter of settling up. Smoking—drinking too . . .

On other days, I contemplate, bewildered, the sky renewed by spring and the sun—how indecisive they are, floating like a great blue and gold dream. Or I pick wallflowers from a flower-bed and scatter them to float—for the sake of contrast—in the stagnant water of a bucket swarming with monads and bacteria; but a dancing sunbeam sprinkles that putrescence with emerald holes, in which, in accordance with billions of facets, little diamantine wings palpitate.

In the evening, I take pleasure in the concert of toads, which spin out the notes of oboes and respond from one meadow to the next. Anything, in sum, rather than confront that blanched old man crouching in the depths of a Vatican of shadows, patiently awaiting his hour: my genuflection and my kiss on his slipper—anything, rather than that sinister pontiff whose infallibility I deny: the consciousness of the Real, and *its* cardinals: Ennui.

My pilgrims in red cloaks progress along a road with burning ruts. "Most dear, do not stray either to the right nor the left. To the right you would roll down a bank of polished steel all the way to a canal where obsolete magi are dissolving, and whose green cloudy water causes loss of memory. To the left one dies because of a young witch garlanded with celery and asphodels who will feed on your heart if you allow yourself to be tempted by the rhythm of her fluid march through the sabers of the nenuphars, which she has sown in order that one's feet are lacerated in coming to her.

"Good pilgrims, always advance straight ahead in the middle of the road; pilgrims of my desire, march with eyes fixed on the golden cupolas and bronze towers of the proud city in which my bells are ringing the Easter of renunciation, where glorious hymns are thundering in the basilica of which I am the Titurel."[1]

From the earliest years of childhood (now more than ever), I have had a dream of the motionless white cold of the North, where no one before me had ever left the imprint of his footsteps.

Exquisite joys! To go all alone thus, for weeks, beneath the polar night illuminated at intervals by the silent fireworks of the aurora borealis; to laugh at the snow in oblique flocks of butterflies brushing me and caressing me and draping me in ermine; then stopping to model snowmen that do not melt . . .

Yes, to go North, always, with no other goal than to go there.

Then the dream becomes anxious; perhaps there is someone at the end of this desert. And, indeed, soon (you know him, plains traveled in a blank slumber) slow smoke spirals on the horizon; a blue-tinted roof gradually grows; I approach . . . there it is!

Inside—also all white—a cabin carpeted with im-maculate satins, an old man is warming himself before

---

1 Titurel is the Grail King in Wolfram von Eschenbach's version of the Grail story.

a violet hearth whose flames tinkle like the notes of a harmonica; so white, so centenarian, so ancestral to me: the Hermit of the Snows. I sit down beside him; we recognize one another without saying anything—and we warm ourselves for centuries and centuries, while a cricket embroiders thin algebras for the usage of salamanders. Outside, the mercury freezes; the wind converses pianissimo with the falling snow; the prodigal manna of a paradise of Cold; large reindeer with silver antlers wander around the house and sometimes risk a velvet eye at the window, belling softly . . .

It is so calm—whiteness until the awakening!

Those eyes, oh, all the female eyes, mazes in which my idle thought amuses itself.

Those: an altar of aventurine velvet constellated with roseate fires; and what vision—among the grave sounds of a horn—of a tower, a golden lion and drowsy sand, where a persecuted chatelaine is desolate; mandoras strummed by the insouciant fingers of divided pages; the palfrey of a Dark Handsome Man[1] whinnying at the tower . . .

A little ballad, those eyes; but that is good, and the altar saves everything.

Those, which only a mind apt to cultivate Hysteria in a befitting manner can understand; those so many morbid nacres and shadily phosphorescent burgundies,

---

1 "Beau ténébreux" [Dark Handsome Man] became a popular phrase in French literature after its use in the French translation of the pastiche chivalric romance *Amadis de Gaula*. Its English equivalent, commonplace in fortune-tellers' patter, carries similar implications.

devil's lanterns—angry because She has not been able to violate the ultimate Grail; the proud crystal and steel soul of our most recent Parsifal . . .

You, a long time ago, one evening in a faubourg in merriment.

Others, whom the fay Melancholy never touched with her wand, mirror their unconscious cruelty; grim metals in the radiance of other stars, whose unusual flamboyance no spectroscope can fix. Before them, at certain feverish hours, it seems that the wind of the unknown comes to pass over our forehead . . .

The excellent person is unaware of her eyes.

And others, and others: vibrant sky violated, in accordance with stormy forges, by lighting flashes, long at the horizon but which attenuates, very bright, into loose strings of peals toward the heights. Abandoned garden, entirely impregnated with autumn with pathways garish with dead leaves, and where, furthermore, an arrogant folly agitates little bells in order to drive away the soul of weary Erigone, who is striving to remain drunk— there . . . Convulsive waves, heavily green-tinted, palely cadaverous with the rise of a malefic moon—and ulterior gulfs where serpents coil and basilisks hiss . . . Others, so remote, blue clashing swords—then calm panoplies that are overturned again—if she mistrusts herself—by the rancor of a Valkyrie . . . Oh, all Their eyes, well-known, too well-known, waltzing and fulgurating around my thought . . .

But silence, and abrupt darkness . . . What is happening, for the Night to steal away thus before a sudden splendor?

Her eyes, the eyes of the very dear child light up amid the desolation of the early morning! Divinely somber lake, lake thrice pure, quivering with impalpable white vapors that flee and silver—oh, distantly!—a missal dawn. Queen Sadness sits on the edge of those melodious waves, weaving I know not what desperate golden cloth and remains mute and in profile because doves that fly away never come back again . . . Oh, to drown one's heart in those eyes; to lose oneself therein, and collect from the lips a little of the sob of a chorus of stars scattered in the sky that is fading away so madly in the depths of the mysterious lake . . . This is the coveted Dream, the charm and the grace of the infinite—and my soul can no longer escape the nets that Her gaze extends, and my own eyes are two irreparably tarnished mirrors; for I am blind, for having reflected those eyes too much.

Real life floats around me like a funeral veil.

Now, I no longer recognize myself very clearly—so weary, run aground on this faded divan, whose springs utter groans like a heretic put to question. The odor of an ancient crime is stagnating in the room; the curtains resemble tearful relatives around a tomb; the furniture creaks in a troubling fashion; the fireplace where two brands are no longer ablaze chills me. And what, with blurred eyes, is lying in wait for me in the depths of the mirror?

I have a very clear perception of not being here; my Self is vibrating elsewhere—oh, entirely elsewhere; where?

Meanwhile, the creature standing before me runs her teasing fingers through her tousled russet hair; then she picks up her glass—always that infernal alcohol!—and clinks mine, which is still on the table.

"Come on, drink; what are you thinking about?"

"Nothing. I'm cold and I'm drunk; you must have noticed it."

"Bad temper! But what are you looking for? Can't you hear the rain falling? You're not going out in this weather?"

I empty my glass without responding and I look around: what distress there is in these things! And me—a hunted wolf, I tell you, a true wolf . . . That individual in the mirror annoys me.

"But what are you thinking about, then?" she resumes, parting the folds of the peignoir that veils—very slightly—her royal tawny nudity.

"Oh, no, enough for today, my charitable friend . . . And then, if you want to know, I'm thinking about my double black star, the dear evil star from which I was exiled a long time ago . . . if you knew how sick at heart my heart is!"

"It's me that you're telling that to?"

"To you; so I think it futile to embroider the theme further; I have too many obligations to distress you with my distress—I'll go . . . I'll return to my island . . . you know: my island! Anyway, I like the rain a lot."

And I go, without saying any more, tottering slightly, while she, so tranquil—indifferent?—lights a cigarette.

I'm glad not to have stayed . . . I'll soon be back, however—for sure.

An implacable scribe—Asmodeus—installs himself in a vast room haunted by all the demons of Impurity. On granite tablets, with a stylus of iron, he records the sins committed in so many evil places from which he lifted the roof while my soul was soiling itself there. On certain evenings I felt some alarm in contemplating the cold lamp—so yellow!—that illuminates his sinister task. Not for anything in the world would I risk a glance at that encyclopedia of my villainies—but a mad desire would take hold of me to take refuge in cilices and mortifications if, on reflection, I could not prove to myself that "all that" was not my fault, not truly my fault, given the madness to which I know not what confides my guard, and which it is necessary to distract—is it not?

However, to disculpate oneself thus is perhaps one more suggestion of the demons I glimpse, grimacing from the sulfurous shadows of the room.

What if I were to consult that scribe . . . ? I forgot that, to my misfortune, he is mute and deaf. Come on, my gentle madness, I believe it's preferable to go back *down there*, whence we came.

Will these things have an end? My Self weighs upon me horribly and I am disgusted by the mocking double that I cause to spring forth so often—like a diabolical jack-in-the-box—in the face of people who believe they have the right to observe me. A chatty breed, they laugh! They find me amusing.

Let us take refuge in the pure nocturnal landscape of a fateful dream.

Under the blue moon, a soft meadow is displayed, where golden campanulas flourish; in the middle, a well hugged by tormented ivy. No noise, not a breath; O realm of Calm!

How many nights have I leaned my elbows on the rim of that well, whose still black water sends back to me, instead of my reflection, the image of one from whom I still await, without any hope of obtaining it, a welcoming smile.

Yes, how many hours toward that magical water . . . I would gladly mingle a few tears therein if I had not forgotten years ago the manner that one adopts here in order to weep . . . Or throw myself in the well? But the image would break up; and then, an order emanating from Her eyes—somber calices—throws me backwards. Then I sit down in the perfumed grass of the sleepy meadow; I surprise myself picking a bunch of golden campanulas, which I raise in oblation to the moon—the very amicable moon, which brushes my lips with the kiss of a blue, chastely cold radiance. And, a caressant rhythm, the soul of the campanulas sings in the depths of my heart.

O compensation!—no matter that I am very ill . . .

Now, quotidian life carries one bier more: the Reaper is leading the mourning in person. And the passers-by, astonished by the candid drape strewn with peacock's-eyes, cry out: "What's this, then?"

Not much: yet again, some too-well-born soul returning to Limbo.

SHADOWS ON THE WALL

The sad hour in which each in his turn goes away.
VICTOR HUGO.[1]

---

1 The quotation is from the play *Ruy Blas* (1838), from a key speech by the eponymous character..

THE LEGEND OF THE GOOD PAUPER

THAT SINGULAR PAUPER—dressed, moreover, in azure and gold, who glorified himself with a large peacock feather in his hat—had the idea that he would go to sit down at the door of the church where Friar Lawrence married Romeo and Juliet.

"They are good young people, so I will gladly give them the alms of an advice—provided, of course, that Mademoiselle Capulet remains strictly veiled; for I am fatally constituted in such a way that encountering the gaze of a virgin solicits within me I know not what Prince Charming of whom I would very much like to be rid. It is irresistible and very annoying, piping madrigals scarcely being my forte any longer. As well demand the gnarled trunk of an age-old willow to star itself with tea-roses within twenty-four hours. I know, of course, that the tea-rose had, at one time, the very tint of my soul, but today it struts in the livery of the Green God, and I wish Queen Mab might carry me away . . .

"*Consummatum est*, here come the newlyweds!

"The little fool! She's lifted her veil . . . In truth, I'm not too annoyed; such warm gray birds are frightened in her gaze that one has to forgive her."

The Pauper advances, hat in hand—the extravagant peacock-feather sweeping the dust—and, fixing on the nocturnal spouses a gaze in which a stray rays of Sirius persists, says: "My good monsieur, legend would like this entire ceremony to end quite tragically, but don't worry, nothing like that will happen, in spite of the tales of a certain Shakespeare, who, be warned, has given the genre a masterpiece by transmuting your story . . . what a surly individual! Personally, I'm more serious, and . . .

"Confide your hand to me, my good monsieur; for the price of the misadventure that I'm going to relate to you, I only ask for one of Madame's smiles."

Romeo—in a doublet the color of that calm summer midnight—was nonplussed, but he held out his hand.

"Green God who adores the souls of frail lotuses, and you, Saturn, his dear planet, inspire me! All in all, Monsieur, you are fated to end up very foolish and very old; you will lose your illusions, and, above all, sums of money, and within a year you will be neglecting Madame to run around the taverns. Sometimes, also, you'll be the thin man who serenades beneath ingrate balconies. It will come about that you'll be unable to pay your rent and you'll be wearing frayed gloves. You'll regret, then, the prebend with which you've gratified the worthy Friar Lawrence, but—too late. Nevertheless, between now and then you'll have three months of agreeable sensations on the bed—said without offending Madame . . ."

Turning to Juliet, he continued: "Your turn, my child. You'll die young; so much the better, for there will be solitude and ennui. Oh, you think it's sufficient to per-petuate yourself, smiling and tranquil; to be there, in a freshly-washed pink peignoir, always docile to the kiss but not having the genius to offer it first; to prepare for your husband's dinner—he'll often come back late—innocent but exquisite polenta; to sleep all night long—without snoring, it's true—in the utter quietude of your serene conscience? It wasn't worth the trouble of receiving an education as complete as yours, nor, above all, of allowing yourself to be abducted. My child, my child, riotous dark eyes, slightly aslant, will do you a few bad turns, and the result will be—my prediction to Monsieur Romeo . . . I can see that I won't get my smile. Well, weep; the angel who sways in the calyx of your lily will collect your last virgin tears—and that will be counted in my favor on high!"

A deep bow—that, fluttering, the magical peacock-feather directed at the stars—and he fled. And the two lovers, notably bewildered, looked at one another.

"Hmm!" grunted Friar Lawrence. "Some drunkard."

"Ah!" said the Pauper, as he drew away. "I've defended morality; I sense that I have a brand new soul. However, that charming girl has soft gray eyes, and what a pure geranium, her lips! It's necessary that I cure myself right away; I shall sleep badly!"

He went to a bosom friend, a philosopher—and a grocer in his spare time. "My dear Master, give my two sous' worth of resignation." Satisfied, he wandered, digesting the drug, through that pale summer night, perfumed by resedas, sparkling with young stars, until first light, which had the privilege of sending him to bed.

Six months later. The time is dragging, murky and dull, the nostalgic hour when market carts beat time fu-

nereally on the pavements of the suburbs. The Pauper—
in gray velvet simarre edged with ermine, a cock-feather
in his hat—encounters Seigneur Romeo in the depths
of a dubious closet where cabbage soup is sold for five
centimes a bowl, pale, slumped on an empty crate and
devouring his helping of soup. At his feet is a shamefully
disheveled guitar.

"Oh, my dear monsieur, I predicted correctly. Here,
I still have a little resignation; drink it instead of that
Spartan broth. Then listen: it's not the skylark singing,
even less the nightingale; it's the bird the color of infinity
that builds its nest in the mouth of the sphinx, not far
from the old Nile . . .

"You've eaten? Good, then consider a little the amity
that I'm bringing you; Titania's waiting for me outside,
and her emerald winged chariot is getting impatient; she's
taking me to her realm of Fable; rather than live this life
in little daily rainfalls, would you like to go with me?"

Humbly, Romeo follows the Pauper; they go out and
take their places next to Titania. The autumnal Night is
divinely green, around them, and its stars are red, like
tears of blood. And the winged chariot bears them away
to the land where the singing mandrake grows.

Exegetes of dreams, my brothers, imitate them.

YESTERDAY'S DOLL

THE LONG artificial smile circumscribed palely! And such a vacillating gaze elongating like a mass of treetops morbidly gilded by an autumnal sun.

"My gentle boy," she said, "do you remember having loved these reflections of the river in the undulations of my russet hair? This dimple in my exquisitely thin shoulders? Study a little—but what modesty is holding you back? The mist over my veiled eyes, similar, today, to stained glass in November; a priceless little soul is huddling in them. You're silent? An outrageous magnet is drawing you toward cerulean norths. Come on, since your stubbornness is so positive, accept the flower of shadow that hides in the distance of my silkiest flower-beds. You're still calm; don't you know it any longer?"

An autumnal sun is agonizing, all alone, under the trees fatigued by gold; the orange fauna of her eyes vesperizes and becomes redoubtable. O impatient twilight of passion!

"I'm very tired," replies the Pauper, "and an eternal misunderstanding resides in this of which you seem to be unaware. However, examine me; do you not divine that your words are reaching me imprecisely, one might think from far away? An inconvenient fog separates us; I fear that by offering in this fashion your dear little soul—reflect in favor of how ingenious I was, with what absolute brushes, in my illuminating knowledge—you might catch cold. Then again, it's dusk; that's the evasive hour in which I please myself, outside all décor; so remark, oh, remark, that I'm shivering because I feel guilty and worthy of your disdain. If you could only comprehend what a chill emanating from your eyes is striving around my thought. Yes, your eyes . . . ! Add that a sharp wasp is lying in ambush there."

"Oh, shameful Narcissus," she cries. "You'll truly make me regret my dear Papa Coppelius. Come on, deign to take me to the wood; I'll dissimulate my beauty under hyperborean foliage and I'll recite things to you in a familiar voice . . . very good things, since you taught them to me."

"At one time," he replies, "but no, that's sufficient; because of you I howled for a long time under the red whips of the three Megaeras (or perhaps there was only one): Anger, Pride and Lust. Those estates of service . . ."

"Oh, let's go out."

After all, he thinks, following her, *firstly, a delightful bouquet of red carnations is fading in her belt; secondly, her perfume isn't new to me, but might doubtless still evoke a few variegated joys; thirdly, this apartment, in the violet shadow, is populated by troubling profiles and it's better to avoid the teasing of the gnomes that I sense lurking behind the cushions of the divan; and then . . . and then,* vae soli; *I feel, this evening, like an absurdly orphan soul: to entice her would be prudent.*

A fiacre goes by.

"Coachman, to the woods." And they roll, without saying anything.

But she, suddenly: "What, you're not saying anything? Don't you have a provision of sweet talk?"

But the Pauper, cowardly at times, retains his pride today: "My dear, I know not what good genius expresses, into the cup of my mind, the juice of green clusters of dreams. What can I do about it? I am, as you're not unaware, the last king of Misty Thule; I have duties. Suffer then, in silence, that I'm establishing you a worthy palace in the mystic sunset floating in your eyes."

"Oh! You're very free!"

"More than you think."

And they roll on, very sagely, amid the titillating peppery scent of captious carnations, and the rising inks of the evening, and the invectives of the city toward the imminent stars.

ONE OF THE PAUPER'S EVENINGS

I ARRIVE—the Pauper with a beggar's wallet full of fake dreams and illusions that will never be valid currency again—at the edge of a perverse green, very correct and slightly sinister orchard, of many well-pruned apple trees whose apples are gleaming like fresh wounds. The sun is defunct; turquoise and amethyst sylphs are closing with golden bolts the doors of a distantly occidental fragile palace. Higher up, a broad bright eye, devoid of a pupil, is vacillating in the sky. Behind me, mauve mists, brown gauzes, are floating over the road traveled—the white dusty road that bears my solitary footprints. The wind is singing sadly in the branches; the wind is telling old, old, forgotten stories.

But I do not listen to the gossip of the wind in the branches; I am the Pauper who empties his wallet on the grass and calculates his receipts of recent days.

Here are the pretty pebbles that a charitable woman gave me, as the rarest jewels in her casket, on the morning that I left her home. Ah, I can still see us before the great fire of soundless pine-cones; me grave, my feet on the fire-irons, entirely in accord with the falsely heraldic armchair in which I was resting my weary vagabond curvature, and reciting—without too much annoyance, believe me—precious nonsense once learned in the school of such extraordinary subtle passers-by; her standing by the fireside, in her loose robe the color of Atlantic waves, biting a lock of her sparse black hair and crying: "But truly, my dear Pauper, you have a singular gaze; one might think it that of a cat seeking to fascinate a tremulous mouse. Oh, I can't tell you how much your eyes attract me, your changing eyes with ruddy reflections, then dotted with gold, and then somberly emerald in the farthest background."

Then the glaucous robe fell and—how did it happen?—the charitable person was in my arms. I believe we pretended, all night long, to love one another very much.

The next day she gave me those stones; I accepted them—everyone knows that I'm a Pauper with no scruples—and I left, but for several days I've had a chill around the heart.

Come on, stones, into the bag!

That opal—let's see . . . yes, I remember evenings—mute evenings of looking at one another, scrutinizing one another, astonishing one another with a perennial wall of ice between us and motionless phantoms that forbade any marriage of our lips. Oh, her bloodless lips and her fine pale hair and her eyes, in which the soul of Saint Cecilia's lute quivered!

When I quit her (soon, for I was becoming dangerously pensive) she slipped me this opal, so dying and so clouded. It frightens me, this opal; and it's never without a tear—for which I mock myself immediately—that I contemplate it.

Here's the cherry-red silk belt, with pasquins and glassware, and fake silver plate. In handling it, what hoarse laughter still croaks in my memory! My God, how she laughed, the very young one, so perversely thin and small, very small, who taught me the equivocal charm of embracing a quasi-adolescent. I incited her to laugh so much—perhaps I was too cheerful with that one—that she died of it, bequeathing me her Sunday best belt.

Into the bag!

Without commentary, the Pauper stirs and immediately rejects a thousand objects: crumpled buckles, extinct ribbons, tarnished bracelets—faded finery, those alms of how many grimacing creatures—without further thought. But suddenly, he extracts from his bosom a locket, virgin gold, which seems a fragment of a star, then hides it precipitately, then takes it out again and exclaims, in a different voice:

"Finally, the unique profile for which red lilies bleed in my heart; in sum, the unexpected, the momentary, the marvel that my dream will halo for centuries. O heartbreak: an encounter, a kiss, a sob and her flight, because the Chimera evoked her elsewhere. Oh, the flame of pity in the somber eyes, an illusory glory of which I'm dying—and only to have had that pity, O little mouth with a sad smile which asked me for forgiveness for my suffering—that she was not cured; O profile loved beyond the Appearance; frail eyes that illuminated you with a child-like, unreal soul!

"That one gave me a little bread, bitter bread! My only nourishment, since she's no longer mine . . ."

The Pauper throws the locket into the grass scintillating with dew. And the locket shines with a sharp gleam, and burns his heart. He gets up; he hesitates, so thin—a submissive melancholy—that he is a shadow in the dusk. Oh, to go away, to quit this orchard where the fruits are as vermilion as raw wounds . . .

But the brightness of gold palpitates toward his heart. Then the Pauper, the illogical Pauper, picks up the locket and kisses it recklessly, shedding a few tears—ridiculous, is it not?

Afterwards, sitting in the damp grass, he devours the bitter bread of jealousy, the black bread of his torment— and then ends up, all the same, falling asleep, rolled up in his cloak.

The wind hums dead songs in the branches; the meadow trembles with wounded birds whimpering. And the Lady of the Night, rising in the sky, takes a malign pleasure in swinging her pale lunar lantern over the shivering Pauper.

ANOTHER EVENING

THE PAUPER, in a linen tunic—as blue as pale as an October sky—sits down on a throne of ice in the palace of the Illusory. Before him are lined up, contained in clay bowls, the reductions of those Abstractions whose scintillation persecuted him when the Summer yellowed the cliffs of our island (so distant!). But they are extinct and recumbent.

He laments in this fashion: Alas, for long years I have been consuming myself in stirring my sentiments in ideas, and no result worthy of pride has recompensed my disinterested efforts, except one that, with the best will in the world, I cannot consider other than a little frightening: every time that it has occurred to me to attempt, in true daylight, a manifestation of the anterior god whose eyes are severe lakes and the hair harmonious forests in the utmost depths of my soul of olden days, someone—a ludicrous madman—has substituted himself for me in order to proffer, via my own mouth, disquieting sentences that drive away from my teaching, appreciated nevertheless, the eventual disciples that I would have liked to convert.

People seem to consider me a compromising person, whom it is better not to frequent; and their attitude signifies an utter scorn. As for me, when the *stranger* falls silent, I emerge from a vertiginous nightmare; I protest, knowing that I have formulated the contrary of my thought—and yet, the repercussion within me of the *other*'s frightening doctrines awakens sympathetic echoes.

If I risk, then, a glance at the mirror in which I survey my soul, I remain stupefied, no longer recognizing it and surprising I know not what redoubtable presence—it is not the god—busy illuminating with pale beacons the contrary arabesques of the Park that contains my most distant Being.

There, a celebration is taking place to which my apparent thought has not been invited; there, a thousand labyrinths of prisms interlace their enigmas, which a transparent fay, beneath a veil that only hides her face—but completely—travels with a limp.

Afterwards, long-striding men come and disperse a gold powder over things, with it would be preferable not to squander thus—at least, that is my judgment today, *and only today.* Then mysterious ladies with unhatched eyes clad in stiff brocades with cold glaucous seams, of an imprecise shade, arrange themselves at the top of a marble staircase opening on to an esplanade that is lost in a night traversed by fluid "possibilities." Several descend the steps slowly, slowly—but how many steps there are before they reach the bottom!

Further away, other little ladies in robes of flaming hope are dancing with one another in counter-measure to the sound of a monotonous music. I do not know the rhythm, exactly, but—as at present—it appears to me to be regulating the variations of a solitary note, sometimes languishing, sometimes febrile, repeated to the point of enervation. (I am anxious; I become impatient; a desire for the light of this place torments me with regard to those effigies out there . . .)

Multicolored lords surge forth sometimes who ask timidly to end the dance, but they are rejected. They draw away deeply saddened, to the point of falling down on the gold-speckled sand and throwing away their neatly combed wigs, which shine like little comets.

From a dark corner an individual clad in scarlet appreciates the savant steps of the ladies. Suddenly—an unknown hour sounds—he approaches one and makes a sign to her. She understands, she stops, and she inclines her head, which he cuts off with a sharp cutlass. All of them are decapitated thus. No blood flows, but their eyes, finally born, blaze: young roses in an estival aurora.

The lords cheer loudly, smooth their recuperated wigs and beckon to the women waiting on the marble stairway. None makes a move; then they dance madly, without paying any more heed to them . . .

Everything is extinguished . . .

I can no longer perceive anything, but the god—who has become very old and is gradually fading away—yawns while fanning himself with an uprooted oak tree; he shouts something to me that I cannot hear; nevertheless, I divine it to be ironic.

When I return to myself, after those adventures, I stagger like a drunken man and I burst into laughter like a rusty weathervane. That authorizes my disciples to throw stones at me and pursue me with jeers. That is why I have retired here, the philosopher of Misty Thule . . .

See how carefully I am numbering these clay vases, in the order conceived by my immutable dream. As soon as it is done I shall write on each one: "Preserves for Posterity."

A PLAINT

LOWER DOWN than the impetuous spring whose tunic is fringed with the claws of brambles—brambles wound around many a decrepit pedestal, and their spiteful jealousies—lower than the yellow-suffering swell of gorse in which our ephebes pamper one another two by two, the muted surbased arches of the crypt wander in the darkness toward a cellar. The memory of a very old perfume trails there languidly and then stagnates, like the moist kiss of a dead lip; at ground level a wretched lamp palpitates, whose flame whines and burns the wings of meager mad moths climbing along the sullen walls; tarnished golds finish the vault with scales, scarcely deigning to reflect the anguish of a dead Eye detained there.

O haggard GAZES! what plaintive phantoms of illusions of old! these glimmers punished for being too obliging in the undulating caress of forbidden rhythms, colliding with one another in the glacial darkness . . .

"Would you care to sit down here, my Master?" Through the judas-hole fitted in the iron door of the cellar we will listen to the struggling Voice.

"Gladly; that can take the place of an examination of conscience."

The gaze—you will distinguish there a derisory crimson and dirty gems—the gaze says: "I am Epimenides, the inconsequent Prince of the pure Lakes who loved himself in his instinctive soul: white rosaries told effusively under the reflective immobility of an interior star." Alas, O clenched memory, I realize my imprudence too late, and that it is necessary to hasten to extinguish at its source the radiance that created for me the primal Arcadias of perennial Tempes, and even radiant future Edens—eagerness floating in a cup of sky in which my ingenuity was intoxicated for centuries!

But you, forever abolished simplicity of blue-tinted landscapes, nocturnal rivers curved like sabers, fresh islets dear to idylls, and the extended arms of naiads, I am no longer the naïve Lynceus of old.

Is it necessary to go up higher, O panting memory? Indra places his luminous feet on the virginal summits; days pass thinking amid the dormant aroma of tulip trees and rhododendrons; and the wind glides in the foliage, an orchestra for the meditation of a word of Gautama. It is an orb of noisy silence in which my thought swings, an adolescent flower . . .

Finally, known footsteps squeaked on the sand; night rose—and smiled, veridically, one with the loving eyes, with the ignorant eyes that were able to evoke in me pleasures devoid of lees.

Those things are dead; and what have you become, my truly too primitive soul of solitudes? You knew the folly of drying up your infantile petals, in accordance with other gestures, and you repudiated the divine Essences that were your icons. But would you have believed that the bleak priapism of today was to come? Would you not have denied then, my soul, the black intoxications, the bewildered aftermaths, the ennui, like a cold rain at daybreak over the feverish?

Thus, sensual sabbats presided by a false prophet always counsel: "Gather, it is the Absolute," furious choirs in which the voice of my sincerity broke; let us conclude: instead of the hoped-for chrysanthemums, I have been lured by the bouquet of nettles; I have burned my fingers thereon and thrown them away—and that is why I am here . . .

"You're lying," cries the Master, finally alarmed, "for there are words that *must not* be spoken; you're lying: at our fêtes, you were heard crying out there—with delight, you claimed, with ennui, we have divined. Then you were warned: choose—either intoxication among our ephebes, provided that you sell us the perfumed lie that your pride names "my primal soul," or silence here, in order that you can, at leisure, sterilely, create the real for yourself. What was your choice? Has it not also been concluded that you will not set up again, to frighten with the dead glimmers of illusion, the passionate processions that guide us toward the altar of the five Sensualities?

"You asked for the shadow; you have it."

"No, you've deceived me. I hoped for the mysterious temple in which I would be the idol saved for appearances and monads, the consented rites of which would be observed by all of you with an entire faith; I believed that I would be adored like a very simple and very sage god . . . Instead of the promised—and due—glories, this cellar, and the Death that is whispering in my ear."

"You're lying; your will made this prison for you; if, on your head, our Island displays its flowers and its sacred woods, if we have built the palace in which we denude the young fays whose sole reason for being resides in our desire, it is because you understood the virtue of your sacrifice; you accepted to be the ascetic who suffers for us . . .

"Today, I know not what echo of laughter from on high is descending to incite you to revolt—needlessly. It is too late; the door is closed, the key has been thrown into the sea; you will not get out."

"I shall be resuscitated; I shall be the canidian moon over your most troubled insomnias; I shall be the silence of your nights and I shall stifle you."

"No," says the Master, getting up, "for I have killed silence."

And he goes away.

Thus, in the depths of a cold crypt, under the most ra-diant palace of my royal isle, Misty Thule sometimes stirs up an age-old argument—and that GAZE dies, slowly frozen, for having plucked an anterior soul.

SENTIMENTAL RHAPSODY

THREE in number, they are sitting in the utmost depths of the somber cadaverous courtyard.

All around them are the walls—as wrinkled as old men—of a ruined palace overhung by shaky cornices, pedestals for such statues, with staring eyes of gold and ebony, and cheeks of green-tinted bronze in which rain glistens. Over the heads of the Three is the insurmountable sky, so high, the wintry indifference of the ruddy sky. The heavy velvet flowers of silence kiss their bitter foreheads; something red and quivering gleams in the middle of the courtyard—and for a long time, thus, the Three contemplate the silence and the cold drizzling rain; and the green-tinted statues make signs to them, lanterns in the troubled sky.

Finally, one of them, handling a tawny bracelet impregnated with distant odors, says: "I have a remembrance of an advent of old; I have a remembrance of little souls down there . . . Four, there were—which we would never espouse—clothed like the sunset; and the gazes that diminish exotic exile; and that delicate slenderness that we loved too much to embrace it; and the anxiety of those long fingers and the suffering—prescribed—of those thin hands, proffered and twisted in importation, toward what divinity? Remember: goddesses of crystal spiraling eccentrically around one another; an oblique sun powders them with fever; they turn, spinning slowly before me; and the sad calyx of their mouth lets fall, amid the bubbles of sobs, words of old of which they do not know the meaning . . .

"Oh, out there in their homeland of blue cupolas and golden towers, a young king is dying because they have departed; a migrating wind is blowing amid his plaint and brings it to us, odorous with regret; palms agitate, which say: no, no, they won't come back again; a strange white flower, grown between the steps of the throne, collects the king's tears and pours them—in dreams—over our hearts in order to refresh them. The king is dying—but the calm lataniers swoon with heavy florescences; censers, in slow enervations of sandalwood and the smoke of cabins, on the shore of a rhythmic sea, tremble in the evening . . .

"Where are the four little legends and their languid eyes of exile and excessively ancient rotes? Where are the figurines of sick gold, so upright in the twilight, so thin—toward which our desire does not dare . . . ?"

That sinister red thing in the middle of the courtyard darts a flash of lightning and palpitates recklessly.

Another; he is agitating faded flowers and crumpled sheets of paper on which honest feminine lies are inscribed: "My desire trails, my desire is a swan with mutilated wings, in a darkness devoid of hope . . . Where is the child, the fay-child whose pale hands would bandage my folly? Where is the infantile laughter that passed by amid the snow of camellias and lilacs? Where are the somber talismanic eyes, mortal delights, the homeland of my soul for a night and a day? Where is my Lady who adores the Chimera? Elsewhere, far away from me, and her aureole of unreal butterflies, and her lips extended to the unknown god . . . And I am a defunct glory, since her eyes will no longer light up in my dream . . ."

The thing bleeds, and bleeds: a river of turbulent blood into which the rain splashes—and the thing is lying like a cadaver.

The third: "I would like to drive away this music, this fairground music, and the clinking of deceptive glasses—and also all those Women whose empty eyes are prowling, surprised, around my sadness, because of their noisiness, which is striving to be joyful. Shut up, tumult of specters, lies that attract me involuntarily; and you, gazes fond of defaming my dearest relics . . . How can I flee? Where can I flee? My soul is agonized by anguish, and cannot . . . Oh, how I would like to chase away these hasty shadows, avid for the blood that is flowing here . . . The bitterness of a fruit of sin resides on my lips, which they brush, those shadows . . .

"How I would like to be alone, to forget the mercenary hours and the identical kisses—oh, alone!—far away, even from you, plaintive brothers—to wash with the waters of melancholy my soul drunk on disgust . . . But what a din reverberates turbulently in the dirty echoes in which my thought is entangled, obstinate toward the past! And not to be able to forget . . . However, I sense myself flowering, a lily utterly alone in a marsh."

The thing is extinct, as dull as last year's ashes.

The sky darkens over the ruined palace; the statues vacillate, crumble and disappear in the wind; the rain streams; icy crepes reign over the walls; the flowers of silence shed their petals, languidly, one by one . . .

And, princes in Hell, three memories eternalize, seated around my heart, shiver and become desolate—nostalgic forever.

FULL DREAM

Dreaming is a second life . . . We cannot determine the precise moment when the self, in another form, continues the work of existence. It is a vague subterrain that is gradually illuminated and from which are disengaged, from shadow and darkness, the pale, gravely motionless figures that inhabit the abode of limbo. Then the tableau is formed, a new brightness illuminates and causes those bizarre apparitions to play; the world of Spirits opens for us . . .

GÉRARD DE NERVAL.[1]

---

1 The quotations are taken from *Aurélie, ou le rêve et la vie*, a quasi-autobiographical fantasy posthumously published in 1855.

FRONTISPIECE

NOW to bathe oneself in the radiant river of a star!
It is mine—I want it to striate the pale ages,
To her, the proud current toward the city framed
By a noisy rampart of floral delights.

Guard of the bell tower, archer, dart your arrows:
My red baying pack is clawing the crenellations—
But rather flee; already my high flames are licking
Your weak wall, where a flock of crows is circling.

Meanwhile, very gently—to the music of palms!—
Solely amorous of the black tulip.
I water the garden of my calm florescence
And mirror it in a flood of gold in which silks flutter.

Let it fight far away, my good river of war;
I evoke my tender sky in triumphs of stars . . .
To capture the frail dream of ephemerae
The uncomprehended spider has spun her web there.

MISTY THULE

IT is very calm tonight! Buried beneath the curly foliage of your hair, slightly intoxicated by your lips and fatigue, I listen to the moist shadow scented with lilac and irises rustling around us. Although my grateful hands still go toward you, my abnormal eyes are enjoying a dance of fireflies on the curtain with an extravagant floral design.

What thought of you—a mystery to me—does the Fearlessness that sanctifies the soul create now, sighing for the flowers picked yesterday and already dying, the fleeting kisses of furtive existences scattered in the eccentricity of this old room, and some gaze of the North and Long Ago, diffused in the nocturnal water of the mirror? What unreal powder frosts your cheeks? And why are the fireflies hastening to suck pollen from the orange languor of your eyes? Can you hear the clock palpitating like a heart . . . ?

O great odorous calm, somber serenity punctuated by errant fires, is this not the untroubled space in which the worlds of fable are elaborated, and those words, icy vertigos of stellar silver, vagabond comets amid the semen of stars, tongues of darkness striped with abrupt phosphorescence, idle fumes emanating from mythical pollens and those spirals of whiteness in palely luminous harmonies that weep in accordance with Aeolian rhythms . . .

✳

The room sinks softly with a gentle movement; suddenly, a profound violet is displayed, swarming with gems issued from perfumed chandeliers, whose fall pauses in order to illuminate the crystals of frail stalactites.

A new day appears; the seconds are hours . . . it is Elsewhere, so epicene choirs affirm, improvising on a theme of yesterday—or tomorrow; and perhaps it is nowhere, save in ourselves, that the very distant Unknown looms up under these arches, sonorous by virtue of the battling waves of a nearby rising tide.

The curtain rises. I suppose you to be the polite fay waiting down below, on the threshold of several stages and pinkly marmoreal palaces, among blue-tinted territories ringed by sparkling scales.

✳

Listen: it is an isle so lost in the depths of the boreal sea that it requires *us* to know it. No ship's prow has violated its unique beach; a proud Virgin draped in a tunic of yellow furze and moaning firs, haloed in the afternoon by the lukewarm caresses of a sober sun, girdled by nacreous cliffs where the rearing cavalcades of waves brandish their standards of seaweed angrily in vain, legendary, in sum, and nostalgic for good poets, it is Misty Thule.

Parsifal adores the Holy Grail there; the melancholy James[1] takes as witness to his rancor the trees of the forest of the Ardennes and mocks the horn of Oberon imploring fleeing Titania; Ligeia teaches metaphysics to the student Nathanael; leaning over a balustrade garlanded with ivy, Melusine shreds camellias whose petals Astolfo, descended from his hippogriff, collects devotedly; Sylvie and Aurélie sit down at the Round Table in order better to hear an oracle of the enchanter Merlin; and ingenuous Pierrot meditates a cosmic pagoda where the Moon lodges. Even the Bird the color of time chirps very fine things in the branches; Caliban, if he is not snoring and dreaming of full bottles, makes Atta Troll dance; and Peter Schlemihl has recovered his shadow . . .

Oh, you know it as I do, that really is our Island. You remember: so many reveries lost beneath the whistling colonnades of the firs with robust scents, so many wandering in the undulating gold of the furze! The feeble sun kissed without offending it the amber silk of your epidermis, and your eyes—divine changing gardens— challenged the similar waves of the lamenting sea. And then that Ocean, my Mind, in which your pride was swallowed, grew and signified. You were the Queen, I was the King; in order to please me, you sang the poem of the Willow Leaf or the lay of the Beauty who Broke

1 "James le mélancolique" [the melancholy James] is featured, along with Titania, in the chapter in Théophile Gautier's *Mademoiselle de Maupin* that describes an exotic fantasy play. The other literary references are mingled, Ligeia from Poe, Nathanael from Hoffmann, Astolfo from Ariosto, Sylvie and Aurélie from Gérard de Nerval, Atta Troll from Heine, Peter Schlemihl from von Chamisso, etc.

her Mirror; and through the verdant maze of pathways, we went forth, in an estival glory expanding over the ages, O Queen, O King, saluted by the barely whispered cantilenas of the spirits of the afternoon, in that fortunate Island, our kingdom: Misty Thule . . .

✳

The chandeliers are extinct, the choirs silent . . . it is cold . . . Centuries have gone by, I imagine, for I have felt very old for so many yesterdays . . .

My God, no, it's the room—not at all fateful—and the bed. Nothing is divinable any longer but the pallor of sheets and your slumbering face and those chimerical curtains, collapsing domes, and the Night in which I am pleasantly enlaced: the tenebrous waves of your scented hair.

But listen again: the cock is crowing; the countryside is waking up, stretching and shivering; the dew is tinkling softly in the grass . . . and the sun of Floreal is laughing in golden rays through the Venetian blinds.

EVENING TWILIGHT

A T THE END of certain days the room is even sad-
der in which a soul reigns temporarily saved—but
at what cost!—from the variegated eddies of Illusion.
Therein are obscure presences that make signs, the indifferent attitudes of weary Floramyes,[1] a heaving leaning
mass of calcined ideas, dreams that are suffocating an
atmosphere of an eternal storm that never bursts, and
rivers without goals, with the stupid expectation of a fer-
ryman whose boat might sink to the bottom one of these
days. Around, the fictitious and shifting décor that the
wide open window reveals, the scarcely resigned exile of
Mongol hordes populating the occidental grayness of the
wallpaper: ever-tangled manes in helmets, empty quivers,
rusty sabers with half-effaced damascenes, patched yellow
robes woven at leisure by the oblique females left behind
in Samarkand—but also, sometimes, the not-quite-
extinct gazes in which the ferocity of a Genghis Khan
roars, and the laughter commemorative of towers built
with human heads, and the echo of the gallop of Tartar

---

1 Floramyes, temptresses akin to lorelei and sirens, are referenced in
several Symbolist works.

horses through a desert, aggravated by the cowardly yapping of jackals.

Oh, dead of thirst, all those adventures!

There remains this room. One would willingly yawn before the painful engravings, the meticulous furniture, the florid upholstery of the chairs, the pitiless diamond shapes of the carpet, were it not for the mirror, the mystery of gold and shadow that is splashed by the blood of a massacre scattered in the dusk—were it not for two souls that are coldly murdered at length there, and if one of them had not taken the trouble to survive, on condition of being a specter—a tearful, famished and angry specter.

No element of interest is also furnished—it is necessary to realize—by the poorly embalmed cadaver that is lying somewhere—but where?—and whose fetidity triumphs over hasty aromatics; its eyes have sunk into the cheeks and are stagnating, green-tinted; they recall nevertheless the glacial distress appropriate to my conscience, whether it be the henceforth-dormant water of an abandoned well or the floating Past, as bitter as sage.

It is entirely the room—or the soul, obsolete murderer of itself, determined not to favor the blossoming of the anemic anemones of fantasy and to close its ear to the sinister evocative speech that the febrile malaise of twilight wants to whisper. Too many fraternal revenants, if one doesn't watch out for them, believe themselves authorized to mutter sentimental rhapsodies like that, of which one cannot make anything. In any case, the key to their charades is lost.

✳

But outside? Outside, the sky is pale silver, light crimsons, paltry sulfurous satins, moving in gentle undulations toward the coppery horizon. Here and there, fabulous caravans of clouds, agates and beryls will subsequently become wild horses carrying the Valkyries of dream to the Valhalla of the stars.

At that moment, the lazuli splash of trees against the occident is disturbing, like a presage; very savant initiates, they file regretfully before the acuity of my perception, sometimes stopping to exchange tenebrous confidences; then they incline at surprising angles and delegate twigs to reveal to me the supreme arcana of vegetal esotericism. Then the wind runs, sniggering, for the four corners of space and, like a mad thing, shakes and flagellates hectically the academic gravity of oaks, the pale slenderness of birches and the tangled hair of willows; great sleeves devoid of arms are shaken, tattered flags flutter and struggle, the unsteady hands of drunkards brandish impotent weapons.

Finally, a great calm . . . then that absurd clamor in which so many resentments are summarized, whispered in momentarily lowered voices: "Nature is a MONSTER!"

I almost knew that; and I feel some esteem for her in consequence; in future she will appear to me less solemnly empty; perhaps I shall even condescend to gratify her aspects with some evocation.

Now come here, my Beloved, little cruel beast, with your shiny teeth like daggers in your partly-closed mouth, and your eyes, which for me are the great astral Night. Look at the sunset: those royal fabrics that are stained, that convulsive desolation of trees prey to the malign embraces of the Wind, those flowers proffered like screams; does all that Nature, a permanent torture and ugly suffering, not teach you anything? Don't you feel a little pity? No—you're laughing. Shut up, then, and stay still, there, in an aura of shadow and gold and bloody mist, included in the mirror . . .

Placid, instilling in me the ignorant splendor of your eyes, you reflect miraculously—in Appearance—I know not what very ancient soul huddled in the depths of my being, whose awakening often recites strange litanies slowly. That is happening, I believe, long ago, at the dawn of the Aryan centuries, one evening in Pamir, by the nascent full moon (the moon as sad and icy as my conscience)—the sky still streaming with the clots of a bloated sun. Standing on the high place where the inextinguishable flames of the sacred fire are blossoming in an odorous blue bouquet, I am the Seer; I am intoning the infinite hymn of Essences and Forms; my heart, torn from my breast, is being consumed on the altar; and a melancholy priestess, upright and pure in the virginity of her white robe, hands me the cup from which I drink, for the sake of future avatars, with the scorn that the Actives of my race will fatally heap upon me, the obstinate amour of the only Dream. And that altar is you; my heart is you; the priestess is you—as is the magnificence of the mortuary hymn, of which you represent the ultimate strophe, in its irreparable perfection . . .

All these things, yes, but without you knowing it—that is even why I love you, my child.

ALLEGORY

THAT NIGHT, under *another* sky, in the realm of Silence and Death, on the river Lethe, there is a silver boat with violet sails, agitated by no breath of wind, as solemn thus as the furled wings of an archangel in repose. A tall figure, draped in mourning, with the proud pale profile of a goddess, her forehead wreathed in gold, is stationed at the tiller: Meditation. An ingenuous bouquet of adolescents is grouped at the prow, in green robes girdled in crimson, shedding white roses over the waves, or gathering the reflections of stars in the palm of their hand; they are smiling mysteriously and looking at one another, knowing the mysteries, without speaking. In accordance with the almost imperceptible current of the river, the boat advances slowly toward a goal designated by a patch of somberly luminous blood on the horizon, in the motionless mist; twelve black swans are floating in the wake.

On the banks—illuminated by the high livid flames of torches proffered by giants of bronze—all of Fable is waiting: to the right, the Olympians shaded by the wingspan of your eagle, O Father Zeus; to the left, the gods of Runoia,[1] and, like the widespread hands of night, the crows of Wotan; further away, toward the hermetic shadow, the Being of Elohims, Yahveh, is fading away; the dolorous face, with its flagellated red-raw, of Jesus is covered with tears that hollow it out and deform it; but the forehead of Cakya-Mouni is radiant, like a buckler of sunlight.

The boat reaches the horizon; crimson sheets are deployed over the waters; a melancholy demon with sapphire eyes opens an ebony door; a mouth of darkness gapes; with a sudden din of thunder and cataclysm, the boat is engulfed therein, along with fearless Meditation, the insouciant adolescents and the twelve swans. Then the door closes again—forever, one divines. The gods are smoke in the mist.

And on the inert river Lethe, over the realm of Silence and Death, other stars spread their unknown light, coldly.

---

1 In the poem by Charles Leconte de Lisle "Le Runoïa" in *Poèmes barbares* (1862).

VISIONARY VISITORS

SLACKLY extended, hands here and there, drowned eyes turned to the window whose poorly closed curtains allow a peaceful ray of the light of the full moon to filter through, I hear, dying within me, the last waves of a Will that is idling in the strike of the Unconscious, and which will soon be so completely abolished that I will only remain an idle reflector for the variegated caprices of Dream.

A foggy atmosphere fills the room; forms blurred by a gray personal light are floating everywhere; some are thin and serpentine, in meanders that touch me and then draw away as if afraid; others, motionless, are grouped on the ceiling, head down, in a bizarre chandelier with a hundred menacing or benevolent faces that dot the phosphorescence with unquiet pupils. At times, with a sweeping gesture, I disperse the appearance of one of those phantoms; then it splits, and one lamp more joins the others. It's not importunate—on the contrary—that numerous blinking above me: something like a very gentle wind, charged with the unreal, passes therefrom through my hair, electrifying me all over.

Now the moon becomes blinding; it is there, directly in front of me, so round and so old or blue, in the gap in the curtains; a ladder of polished steel with diamond rungs is designed between her and me. Is some adventurous selenite about to descend? I desire it so strongly that, in fact, five women in silver robes, very young—with an eternal youth, one divines—in spite of their white hair, slide along the ladder and, their arms graciously interlaced, place themselves before me as lunar Graces.

One of them says: "I command the gazes of Humankind, I am the one who lives in the eyes; it is by virtue of my benefit that you shiver when the Beloved deigns to spread over you the forbearance of a gaze moist with grateful sensuality—but I am also the angry black flame that she darts at you in your quarrelsome evenings."

Another: "I have given your Beloved the perfume that maddens you if you lean over her perfumed cleavage or her most secret beauty; it is thanks to me that she evokes for you a bed of irritating flowers, mingling the somber scent of almond with the rude effluvia of a panther-skin."

Another: "Your Beloved's breath of dying violets is still wandering over your lips; it is me who, when you marry your tongue with hers, makes you a saliva as flavorsome as the juice of raspberries."

The fourth: "Over the slow caresses of your hands roaming upon her body, and the feverish curiosities of your seeking fingers, as they linger in the rebellion of her elastic hair, and slide into the shadowy coverts where a quivering corolla opens, I preside."

And the last: "Do you remember her voice? You compared it to the flights of golden fays and you said that they were tinkling cymbals made of stars. But do you know to whom you owe the Beloved's voice?"

I was about to thank the amicable goddesses and assure them of my gratitude when, suddenly, they shrank, diminishing, and there was soon nothing before me but five large vases of white porcelain circled by green rings, from the slender necks of which effused the thin swirling smoke of incense . . .

A figure sprang from the floor: a white shroud emphasized her frightful thinness—she was nevertheless very beautiful, and very pale, and I know not what nocturnal ecstasy was dormant in the depths of her bright eyes. "I am Death," she murmured. At those words the moon fled, and the nebulous host encumbering my room disappeared. An opaque night reigned.

I was in an amber room whose translucent walls permitted me to distinguish busy people coming and going in other rooms, and others that extended as far as the eye could see. What were they doing? Nothing of which it was possible for me to take account; they were passing one another by, exchanging silent handshakes; that was all.

A voice said to me: "They're the adolescents of the Great Isis; idler, won't you imitate them? If you desire,

I'll recall the phantoms that enlightened you just now; they'll teach you the religion."

"I'd like that," I replied, "but I can't move." In fact, I felt frigid and rigid; my petrified limbs opposed any whim of movement; and then, the mere idea of disturbing myself caused me an insurmountable fear.

Renouncing vain efforts, I tried to think . . . Death! That word never strikes my ear without a frisson of pleasure running through me. To be dead must be so agreeable! It evokes for me a vague and diffuse existence, an obscure flight in accord with strange rhythms, a finesse of perception so acute that I could, for instance, hear grass growing—and the faculty of witnessing, invisible, scattered above things, meetings of living beings, and even participating in them by means of somber suggestions. But perhaps I was already dead?

"Do you think so?" someone whispered.

I turned round abruptly; it was my room as it was every day, but crouched in my armchair, clad in gray, was an individual whose magnificent prominent forehead, beneath curly brown hair, shone with a fantastic light.

"How do you feel?" he asked (his toneless voice seemed to resonate in my chest).

"I'm cold, but what does it matter to you? And how did you get in?"

"I didn't come in through the door, be sure of that; I've been examining you for a long time."

"Who are you, then? The Devil?"

"Oh, no—I have no connection with the old gentleman. I'm Edgar Poe."

"Right," I said. "And where have you come from"

"From there," he replied, lifting his index finger.

I looked up; the ceiling was open; in the utmost depths of the sky, a solitary star was blinking strangely.

"Since my death," he went on, shaking his head in a disenchanted fashion, "I've been living there; already, when I lived among you, I'd visited it sometimes, and I collected the lessons there that permitted me to write my *Eureka*. At present, I know every last corner of it; I'd like to go elsewhere, much higher—but I died too soon."

"Oh! What if you were to take me to your star? I'm sure that I'd be very pleased there."

"Well, then, follow me."

Getting up, he went to the window and launched himself into the sky. I tried to follow him—impossible to move; a thousand bonds tied me to the divan. A being with the face of an empusa weighed upon me, gripping me by the throat, singing in a saturnine voice: "You shan't go! You shan't go! You're not dead—do you see the presumptuous little fellow who thinks he's dead?"

"Let me go! Let me go!" I cried, struggling. Wasted trouble; vain effort; the bonds tightened, and I was cold—cold!

I tried to strike the demon: I could only give the wall a thump that hurt me a great deal. I fell back on the divan, the springs of which grated as if broken.

"Hallelujah! Hallelujah!" sang infantile voices . . .

✳

A being with haggard eyes appeared, clad in a hyacinth robe that fell straight, without pleats, and trailed on the floor; his disorderly blue hair hung down over his face. He looked at me obliquely, laughing sardonically. A red crown of thorns circled his neck and was gradually tightening in order to strangle him. He didn't seem to notice it.

"I'm the angel of Heresy," he said.

Then against a golden background, a crowd climbed a fiery staircase, extending supplicant hands toward God the morose Father: Dominicans, discalced white friars, monks of every sort, Carmelites, Benedictines, nuns of every order. "*Parce, domine!*" they moaned.

"No," cried the angel, "I don't want your prayers—we're all damned."

Somber clouds descended and veiled the face of God; there was a thunderclap, and sinister lightning pierced the angel. He fell.

"Hallelujah! Hallelujah!" sang the infantile choirs . . .

A black Ocean with deformed waves became choppy under an icy wind. All the supplicant hands of the monks and nuns floated to the surface—nothing but the hands. As if weary of imploring, they turned to one another and, clawing at one another and knotting themselves together, their fingernails bleeding, their fingers livid, they tore at one another furiously . . .

The wind falls silent; the Ocean calms down and slumbers, flat; a snow of doves, with pink beaks and feet, flies in a circle above us. The sun surges over the horizon; a distant reef dominates the waves, and a tall column rises, on which Simon Stylites, with tears in his eyes; repeats: "The times are accomplished! The times are accomplished!"

But Christ is marching over the calm waters; the doves fly to him, settling on his shoulders and his hands, pecking them and cooing amorously; he smiles and kisses them . . .

Then everything becomes confused; a garden of roses and magnolias in flower extends before me; and in every calyx, a child with gold and white wings is huddled, and singing: "Hallelujah! Hallelujah!"

I return to myself; my cigarette is extinct, and also the lamp. Now, it's my room, nothing more, nothing less. I feel very tired and very vague . . .

"My God, I'm thirsty!" I cry.

NOCTAMBULISM

AT NIGHT, the windows look at you as if they wanted to confide a secret to you. And in the distant street there is a glaucous flow of aquamarines reflected from façade to façade all the way to the river that turns, slowly sipping its carrion—the river, a singer with arches and bridges, the river into which the bloody knives of old butcheries have been thrown. How it quivers, boiling because of the gigantic furnaces buried in its mud, plumes of russet and reheated vapors daring to the point of dirtying the sky and invalidating your laughter—stars. Fortunately, a wind from elsewhere whips the soiled naiad who is dipping her filthy charms into the river, and permits the chirping of a syrinx among the exiled and sickly trees of the bank. Then, at a gallop, with raucous sounds of the horn, here comes the hunt of a defunct king. Incited, the soul-taker puts his black flute to his mouth, and, proud of defying the wind, evokes in solitude an epoch of which he was . . .

O Grecian waves, sacred waves that circled Salamina and carried floating Delos, swaying, from the Sicilian shore to the promontory of Sunium; O waves, in which the harmony of worlds surprised by Plato's late nights vibrates; O siestas under the olive groves of the Ceramic; O egret of Pallas and the slow rhythm of a procession climbing the Acropolis . . . !

The age-old Theseus, vanquisher of renascent Minotaurs, still being there, I always forget to remove the funereal veils from my galley. Nevertheless, I no longer abandon my eventual Ariadnes; they leave me instead, and they are probably right to take that care.

✳

Tally ho! Tally ho! The hunt is getting excited, and rolling like a thousand devil-possessed cats over the gray roofs, over the sonorous gutters, monotonous scales of which your carapaces are made, for want of anything better, O city.

Let us follow it down below and watch.

The streets are green snakes patched with gold and ridden by thin witches who stick out their tongues at me—flamboyant forked tongues; criminal shells fissured by laughter, in the multicolored sarabands of an alphabet with which they have been tattooed, doubtless to dissimulate their leprosy; rusty midnights are fighting in the overly narrow cages of belfries. A distracted Gargantua is forgetting himself over the city . . .

✳

The hunt is lost in muffled distances. It is raining. A nursling whose mother is refusing the breast is weeping

94

in a mansard somewhere close at hand. A dog is howling, for want of food—it will not have its mincemeat. And now, it is a city widowed of its inhabitants; alone, I am haunting it—my footfalls are clicking there like the castanets of someone dancing away his spleen—and will demolish it tomorrow, given the lack of unexpectedness of its architectures, but, still subject, for hours, to these windows duller than a drunkard's eyes, those windows that are looking at me as if they had some secret to confide to me. Are none of them hermetically sealed, then . . . ? No!

O Night, my somber virgin with violet eyes, carry me to the balcony where the Muscat grapes and the viburnums unwind, over which my Beloved is leaning, toward the very old room, toward the florid curtains that defend, with their perfumed pleats, the slumber of my Beloved . . .

LANTERN SCHERZO

THERE—while they are noisy, unconscious of the clairvoyance that awakens in my eyes like the mists of dream—I perceive my *double*, sheathed in a rosy nasturtium gleam, plunging backwards into a motionless garden planted with cold crystal flowers that interrupt jets of quicksilver, whose rigid flow falls back in somber tinkles into porphyry basins like congealed blood. In the distance, the sky is a sea with eccentric waves on which chimerical blue galleys with golden prows are bobbing. I am less here, among those arguing, than out there, in the intellect of the dominant benevolent spirit whom the crystal vegetation adulates. If I speak—with what a hollow guttural voice!—his reflex, darted in red arrows toward the top of my head, will dictate my opinion.

As soon as it is emitted, I sense clearly that the other, although apparently abnormal and of another rhythm than that of my interlocutors, nevertheless translates the lofty afterthought what they could not formulate—those Artists of the Dream, my peers. In fact, after a surprised silence, at the enunciation of such unusual vocables synthesizing—in sheaves of symbols freed from the matrix of the real—their concept identical to mine, they cry out in astonishment and acquiesce. But I cannot reveal to them the god who, for too-rapid minutes, interposed a revelatory prism between my eyes and the ideal metaphysics; it is only permitted for me to give them a glimpse—how incomplete!—of the host of the worlds Beyond, which a brief incident of the conversation raised up in me; even then, what efforts were demanded of me by the reduced expression of a little of the hurricane of ideas traversing my skull!

The conversation continues, dragging on with a desperate slowness. At the first word emitted by no matter whom, I already know his thought; I could terminate his sentence and complete it—but what would be the point? My Self distracts itself from them more and more, and strives to go higher; a turpentine warmth renders the nape of my neck painful; I no longer see them as anything but a murmurous and diffuse blur; they are far, far away; an enormous and empty Space reigns between us . . . I raise my eyes: large fiery moths are floating above my head, I am drawn up above . . .

Then a city rises with igneous eddies and whistling silks: blue domes supported by silver angels with vibrant wings in which the breezes sing; sidewalks of gold traveled by Beings—very fraternal—whose breath, when they speak, clouds them with a flowery atmosphere; they seem cheerful and offer one another thyrsi with pale green and lilac ribbons; in a square, glass anvils ring under the hammers of ruddy Kobolds; the garlands on the walls of pearly palaces that border the streets are a confusion of interlaced gnomes, who are blowing into little flutes; an orchestra of distant violins rhythms the movements.

It's so happily tranquil, that city!

Finally, the *double* touches my forehead with a hazel wand; my soul launches forth and rises up to blossom over the square in a brazier—rose and nasturtium—where the genteel Beings come to warm their diaphanous fingers—for it is getting cold now. And I sing in a low voice:

Suns of delight setting the roseate ether ablaze.
Flames that were my pure cradle and the theater
Where you caper—alabaster and gold—O verity,
Salamanders, collaborators in the drama, oracles in the hearth.
Mocking follets, ardent charms of tormented snakes:
I am all of you in the Unity.

A voice replies to me:

> *Higher, further, in the crazy Night,*
> *The Unknown floats and the Church flees:*
> *You, your Dream unassuaged,*
> *Chase the Enigma that flies*
> *Losing itself in perilous journeys—*
> *Would you like the fruit that consoles us?*
> *Knock on the golden door guarded by a triple angel.*

Suddenly, everything closes again; a veil of darkness falls . . .

They are there, all of them, very pale and green-tinted, around me, and muttering monotonously. They bore me; my giant Self is stifling here; a desire grips me to knock them down like simulacra of wax . . .

It is necessary to quit them, to go out, to impregnate myself with the soul of solitude.

And I go outside, precipitately.

A singular silence; people flowing like a vain river of shadows; carriages rolling soundlessly; black wadding weighs upon the city; the sun is a congealed cloud of blue waves. The idea springs to mind: Noise is dead! And I burst out laughing at the deduction that the earth is condemned henceforth to eternal silence. Then an immense funeral notice unfolds on which twisted characters appear:

You are invited to attend the obsequies of Monsieur Noise, deceased this evening. Killed by contemporary excess, he was in horror of the Eternal himself. On behalf of the widow, Humanity.

And I laugh, I laugh so much and so loudly that an individual whose path I cross takes offense to the point of asking me whether I am making fun of him. Oh! a terrible chagrin takes me by the throat at the mere suspicion that I might have offended—who knows?—a relative of the deceased; with tears in my eyes, I dissolve in excessive apologies that do not fail to bewilder him further. Understanding that it is impossible for me to destroy his error, I ask him to clarify a suspicion that has suddenly surged forth in my mind: "Pardon me, but were you not, in an anterior existence, a worshiper of the livid Kali? If yes, know that I am the latest incarnation of Vishnu, her age-old enemy."

Frightened, he draws away. As for me, I laugh, and laugh; I amuse myself madly. In the distance, toward the ruddy horizon, gigantic Harlequins deliver themselves to a frantic jig, repeating the refrain: "Noise is dead, Noise is dead." While I try to imitate their multicolored capers, a peripatetician accosts me; this is the fashion in which I hear his invitations:

> "Handsome chevalier who is departing for the war,
> Do you hope to pluck the golden branch?
> Learn that it hardly ever flourishes
>   Except on the heads of the dead."

I do not understand very well . . . nevertheless, I ask him, with an ineffable mildness: "My child, did you approach the Holy Table last Sunday?"

"Get away! etc. etc."

I advance, I advance; the Harlequins have disappeared; a general's hat with a black plume blocks the sky . . . no, it's the Luxembourg and its trees. I approach and lean my forehead on the railings. Immediately, I am a spirit that adverse demons are keeping captive in a great cage. I search for an exit in vain; I strive to slide between the bars—impossible! I am sweating large droplets; I am frightfully unhappy. I decide to leap over the gate (that will be easy for me, because I possess superhuman strength)—someone stops my run-up, a friend.

"What are you doing, my dear?" Ah! The charm is broken! I consider that savior friend who appears to me, with his bistre complexion and dark eyes, as a Malay rajah, and I reply to him:

100

"If you want, O rajah, who are thirsty for lucre
We'll go to Java to plant sugar cane."

He goes away, greatly bewildered. Scornful of him, I continue my stroll; an atrocious fatigue is beginning to weigh my legs down. For hours, eternities now, I try to cross a street; I walk, I walk, I take mighty strides, without being able to advance a single step: always, to my left, is a cap on a toothy and sniggering head—no, it's the Panthéon . . .

Ah! Finally, the street is crossed; how many centuries have gone by in that rude labor? A great many. But how many? That teases me . . . I shall never know, because Time, also, is dead . . . What new currency is in circulation then . . . ? What? What? I don't understand. Oh, yes! Time is money . . . a horrible paralogism!

A matron goes past with a wobbly orange-cart; who is she, that merchant? And I deduce immediately, by virtue of her repulsive, one might say scaly, appearance, and her fur hat, that she was the dragon of the garden of the Hesperides, who, having stolen the golden apples, is lugging them around in life in order to try to sell them and get back enough to offer Andromeda for the necklace of Saint George . . . O confusion: all the legends are amalgamating in my mind.

A prodigious interest attaches me to the monster; I follow it; I look fondly at its oranges; the slightest jolt of the cart on the bumpy pavement clutches my heart—and now I am, myself, the oranges. I sense an intense pleasure in lounging, enveloped by silk paper; soon I am a mandarin wearing mourning for the emperor, sent to the Occident in order to spreads the Confucian doctrine; and from the height of that cart I show myself for nothing to Parisian idlers. A mad desire to talk claptrap to the crowd torments me . . . I take flight.

Let's go home.

Stairways, stairways, stairways! My God, I didn't think I lived so high up; I'll never arrive—inasmuch as the Devil, in the form of my shadow, always adds more staircases to those already climbed. Am I not in the bowels of the earth? Bizarre gleams run along the rocky walls; I can hear the growling of the central fire. Leaning over the stairwell, I perceive Tubalcain the dreamer, leaning on his hammer. And the climb continues, for centuries and more centuries, in which I seem to be dragging heavy phantoms clinging to my feet.

Finally, I arrive . . .

How comfortable I am, lying on my divan! My cigarette surrounds me with aromatic smoke in which a thousand vaporous forms are sketched: fleeting bas-reliefs, in infinite mat ribbons, which retrace amours riding on goats ornamented with ivy and black grapes; galloping pale horses in an ocher steppe; processions of monks swinging gilded censers and green gold banners; a population of harmonious statues; magical ballets collapsing on a terrace of carbuncles in a glory of apotheosis. Finally, the slow ascent of my most intimate Self through blue-tinted clouds: pillows of clouds, blankets of clouds, a mattress of clouds, whose exquisite freshness and lemon perfume procure me an idle pleasure from which I would not want to be disturbed for anything in the world . . .

However, a light wind chases the clouds away. Organs play, very softly; the great nave of a cathedral curves inwards; between the pillars, a radiance falls on the paving stones, alternately gold and violet; no candle is lit, but in that night striated by royal gleams, I distinguish a knight kneeling before the altar; he is wearing a silver coat of mail bordered with ermine; a white feather floats above his helmet—and his hands are extended toward a druid crowned with mistletoe, whose snowy beard comes down to his feet. Standing on the altar, he raises his bloody sickle slowly, slowly . . .

The organs weep broadly; those violet and gold gleams are their harmonies; they descend upon me and clothe me with magnificence . . .

And now I am the marble emperor extended on his tombstone. And until daylight (the frightful, real daylight!) I remain lying thus, heraldic and pious, muttering ancient litanies . . .

MYSTICAL BALLET

TO BEGIN WITH, a pale green meadow, strewn with rosy almond trees with rounded crowns under a milky sky, in which golden aerostats are sailing; and the music of shrill reed pipes swells and decreases—invisibly. The almond trees make hardly any noise, inclining in unison, in the same direction, rhythmically, in accordance with the wind. The sky lowers and fragments. And great white flags float, undulate, and then fall down and cover the green of the meadow—the almond trees are rosier amid that uniform whiteness.

Luminous droplets tinkle and glisten beneath the sheets. Is it raining? I look at the sky; from the nacelles of the aerostats, gold crosses are being thrown: downpours, squalls and whirlwinds of little gold crosses; the sheets are covered by them—the almond trees, powdered with magnificence, are even rosier.

The reed pipes slow down, slow down, agonizing. Bitter fragrances pass in the wind.

Slowly, to the cadence of the dream pipes, the almond trees rotate—then they are dancing girls in pink muslin, with the expressions of martyrs who multiply without prejudice pointes, grand jetés, etc., they pick up handfuls of crosses and let them trickle, golden gleams, between their slender fingers.

Weary of that game, they take one another by the hand; an interminable farandole snakes: the ballerinas, since that growth, extend the charming dwarf tree before my eyes, all the way to the horizon. Cymbals: the ballerinas leap and spin, a rosy round against the opaline sky; the pipes ripple *prestissimo*.

Finally, a large green, pink and white wheel striped with gold, rolls among the aerostats in rutilant zigzags, and its cloud of fireworks, and then encircles me with the rapid curved tresses of a crazy comet.

The pipes die away; night is within me and over me.

CREPUSCULAR FLIGHT

SITTING on the edge of a paradoxical sky . . .
The customary timbres have fallen away, carrying
to cemeteries of silence a few necrophores whose scorn for
such punctual noises cannot be praised too highly. Then,
with convalescent hesitations, a slightly hesitant arietta
rises in the pale air, and creates circular stripes, soon ef-
faced, which my eyes notice in passage, puerile by dint
of attention. A white procession of emaciated penitents
files past, who sign themselves before the Calvary erected
before the sunset. And all those things have happened, I
suspect, in accordance with a strict ritual, in anticipation
of centuries forever and ever black.

But what height! At similar altitudes, one forgets,
passably, the collisions of words and ideas over which one
lingers down below; the philosophical and literary games
of cup-and-ball can go moldy in peace; it's a good bet
that I won't be wearying myself with them any longer, so
sage is my soul and too glad of this bath of meditation,
preoccupied with a vestment in the latest fashion of the
clouds.

Very high, thus, I feel capable of hectic somersaults in the heart of the third heaven—and I can scarcely contain for another minute the impatient tumult within me of I know not what aviary thirsty for fleeting infinity . . . Oh, stop, I tell you! Listen for a moment to my paternal instruction. Futile! My soul is vacillating crazily; the choir of little essential voices is trepidating and demands elsewhere; a string breaks . . . come on, let's go!

Amid the gentle gliding rustle of Bengal silks, a multicolored flock of birds, migratory for the occasion, accelerates toward golden wells, perceived out there, behind the winy distances that totter, drunk on the dusk.

Oh, my vultures with beaks fatigued by carnage, my storks, a souvenir of a recent sojourn in our Misty Thule, you, white blackbird who brought me the rosemary of old legends, you, obstinate robin whose trills galvanize an amour buried in latent darkness, and the morose disenchanted wader who traverses my dreams with long strides like a gray specter, and that galaxy of obsolete pigeons hoarse from having cooed on the altar of a pug-nosed Aphrodite, and how many others . . . !

They leave, they go on, indefatigably. No roof of repose on which to pause between here and there; so much the worse for the belated or the lame. In vain, windmills of Briareus reach out for us; in vain the gibbous fumes of the cities try to frighten us—we do not see them: it is out there, out there, the good golden Thebaid where the inept feverish nullity of beings shuts up, out there is the promised silence, and the hermitage, and the seed of dream and the cup of nepenthe so delicately offered by the charitable blue-tinted hands of a Lady of the Moon . . .

They are far away; but that is only an *avant garde*; you remain, my beautiful bird of paradise, my dear illusion, my resplendent fundamental soul! Go on, fly away, you have to catch up with them . . .

Oh, what a vertical bound: my soul launches forth with a pride that fills the four horizons, and now it is a traveler—far behind the others at first. A new surge: first! So sure of itself, it steers the hurricane of winds toward the golden oasis that resounds with delight out there.

Further forward, further forward! My souls are flying fast . . . too fast, for my eyes are bulging in following you. Moderate your speed, for pity's sake; can't you hear green and red pieces of music swirling in spirals of vertigo, in your pursuit? Won't you let them join you? It would be a glorious offering to the smile of the Lady of the Moon, a few harmonies—my immortal secret—with which it has been pleasant for me to garland you.

But further forward, in the depths of space, far beyond the violet curved distances, all the wings glide—motionless lightning. And finally, the altered flight settles . . . What is happening, then, at the horizon? A pink cloud, a little vapor, a memory—nothing.

An ABSOLUTE GOLD reigns . . . .

"Look out, my dear, you're about to fall in the Seine."

"Oh, my excessively helpful friend, I'd gladly wish you far away."

"I understand; but what interest . . . ?"

"One of those moments, my friend, in which life *has not arrived*."

THE TWILIGHT OF FLOWERS

ALL THE FLORA—as one, which is going to die in the implacable midday sun—from the buttercup to the most extravagant orchids. No human being, no animal; the globe is covered by flowers, with me, the solitary dreamer, in the middle.

I make a gesture; everything darkens; the sun is detached from the sky, it tumbles and flees, a shooting star less and less visible. A wine-lees day stagnates; flowers are tinted with somber violet hues. I try to collect a bouquet; every corolla loses its stem, disintegrates, and falls into fine powder . . .

I close my eyes; a greenish daylight filters through; the flowers grow paler and paler; now they are white, the shades of wax, cadaverous. Wings devoid of bodies open and close—silently . . .

I reopen my eyes: giant rumbling cyclones are circulating, scything down the flowers and carrying them away in a furious waltz. The cyclones gather into one, which comes at me and sweeps me away. I spin, I spin at a crazy speed; the molecules of my body come apart and move in pale pulverized petals . . .

Then a sphere of flowers—white, so icy, devoid of perfumes—gravitates—and me, solitary—beyond the planets, toward the Milky Way, a serpent biting its tail; it surrounds us with nine concentric circles and rotates itself, in the inverse direction to our movement, so rapidly that it seems motionless. Space and time are abolished; perennial cold, gyrating whiteness; me, an incorporeal entity . . .

Everything stops; I fall back—I come back millions of leagues . . .

Three o'clock in the morning chimes; the furniture is creaking strangely; the mirror reflects a bouquet of chrysanthemums that are fading, scattered on the marble of the mantelpiece.

MOROSE

FOR HOURS, plaintive hours (slow and mortally monotonous, like a conventicle humming the insipid litanies of bored and boring bonzes) elbows leaning on a sticky table before a stubborn coal fire—I drink.

It is here, certainly, the shelter in which to lick the wounds of one's heart, where, precisely—a miracle!—a simili-old paper hare brings me another tankard of heavy black beer . . .

Now I drink.

An obsession grows within me and darkens me with an imminent storm; I can't succeed in fixing a single one of my Ideas. As soon as one appears, my anxiety extends its net to capture it unceremoniously, in exchange for pampering it, once seized, weaving it a beautiful cage whose bars are so thin that it will have no suspicion of its prison . . . Vain attempt: the Idea whistles, turns round and flies off to burn its wings in the fire.

O heartbreak! To my objurgations, not the least response, not the slightest sign of attention; a multicolored somersault and then goodnight: "We prefer the ardent tulips of that hearth." My Ideas are badly brought up this evening.

Now I drink . . .

Let's strive to keep our eyes open, let's console ourselves with regard to appearance. I anticipate some magic taking pity on my distress, which will be able to replace, with a hullabaloo of dancing sensations, my fleeing Ideas.

And, furthermore, what good will it do to think henceforth? Is it not preferable to confide the exclusive key to my soul to some dreamery, with no other goal than itself, in which discordant pieces of music will collide, to swoon with delight, marriages of colors that will howl for a divorce and which I shall maintain implacably united? To force my nerves, not sometimes, but always, no longer to be anything but a sick, mad violin over which I shall draw furiously, by way of a bow, the toothless saw of my excessive sensuality?

Now I drink . . .

Let's see, let's see; let's restrict ourselves to appearance . . .

Ah, finally! A ballerina springs from the fire, pirouettes and waddles before me. What bounds! What an insolently red smile in the ceruse of her face! And then, fortunately, she's blind—no, she's asleep—is she a sleepwalker?—and I adore the hermetic fringe of her eyelashes . . . Let her not open her eyes, never, never! Judge, if she suddenly revealed to me black pupils reminiscent of the radiant nocturnal flowers that my soul ought no longer to pick! I'd be induced to think; I'd know once again the obsession (it hasn't flown away; it's asleep)—and I've had enough of that gridiron.

Now I drink . . .

The ballerina spins, spins—a noisy whirlwind that deafens me; the ballerina permits herself extravagant entrechats; sometimes, she leaps so high that she disappears in the sky; when she falls back to the floor she has always unhooked some star, which scintillates in the somber gauze of her skirt.

Thank you, dancer, who brings me thus the fresh kiss, the impersonal kiss of the most distant stars—once dead of chastity . . .

The dancer spins, spins, in accordance with some crazy tintinnabulations; from a new leap she brings back two twin stars: one green in her left hand, the other red in her right. O splendors, apotheoses, seventh paradise of Indra . . . !

Sudden darkness . . .

The dancer is dispersed in the Night; the stars of her skirt rebound into the sky; with shrill sniggers the stars flee, gamboling on spidery feet and spinning, spinning madly, further and further away, as if to sneer at me . . .

It's the tavern, the heavy beer, the fire going out. A "lad" like the blade of a knife is ingurigitating an "old gin" at the counter; a praline commodore is chewing pebbles, flavescent men are reading newspapers; the old hare licks his lips and, winking at me from the wings, beats the retreat on a zinc counter . . .

Me, I'm swaying like a dinghy on the high seas . . . I believe it's time to fall under the table . . .

There! How comfortable it is amid the spittle, one's head on a pile of sawdust! O abjection, baseness, O flavorsome fruits, you'll slake my thirst for no longer thinking.

However . . . listen: an aerial flute has striped the opaque silence (I'm thinking, my God, I'm thinking!); a very pale Idea, dead-blue and yellow as the dust on a dream butterfly's wing, stops and rains warm tears over my face. The flute is weeping . . .

Here comes the secular forest whose branches incline to fan me; the paths converge toward Fafner; Siegfried goes by in a silver helmet, his sword luminous. And the song of the Bird, fluttering amid the flowering hawthorn, languishes, so tender—so tender!

Ah! You remember, my soul: those tears in the eyes of the Adored, those tears, slow, one by one, on the pure white cheeks of the Adored, when Siegfried's bird sang . . .

O sweetness and remission, that memory: flee, somber drunkenness, banal phantasmagorias, bewildered heads that you incline over me. I think, therefore I suffer. But I love my suffering and repudiating the vulgar ambiance, evoking the sole Image, redeeming evil despairs, for love of her, I feel the strength to be again the god who will not die stupidly—ever again!

PASSERS-BY

What would that obstinate heart require,
Unworried heart, what will make it beat?
It would need Queen Cleopatra.
It would need Hélie and Melusine,
And the one named Aglaure and the one
That the Soudan carries away in his gondola.

JEAN MORÉAS.[1]

---

1 The quotation is from an untitled poem reprinted in *Poésies 1886-1896* (1898) p.127.

THE LITTLE GODDESS

OH, the slightly mad countryside where you passed by, my little black and rosy dream—and your laughter, in scintillating sheaves of false notes, amused my ear.

You know our garden of dahlias, primroses and hollyhocks; and the networks of grass and narrow paths; and you, like an Atalanta, with your ringlets of dark hair in the wind?

And then, your laughter again behind the garish trellis of the arbor exuberant with convolvulus and nasturtiums.

At other times, your eyes—that night of unknowing stars—drank the dusk swept with gold and blood around the agonizing sun—red. And you marveled because—like me—you love red; not a certain red, but all reds, whether it be the dusk, or the violent fabrics that your fingernails scratch voluptuously, or, in winter, the berries as bright as the lips of a bacchante—oh, are they not your strong lips?—amid the somber green of the holly.

Do you remember the great silence, as soon as night fell, until cock-crow? Scarcely, in the distance, the whis-

117

per of running water, and the undulating murmur of the slumbering forest; the smoky evening, blue over the mauve meadows chilled by lunar silver: and the crystal cymbals of toads quivering here and there. When you were fearful you huddled against me—you, delicate thin bird—like one who does not dare, you gazed furtively into the shadow. One might almost have been able to imagine that you were dreaming!

All that, all that, is quite dead; dead too the passionate lyre, all of whose strings we caused to vibrate. Since then, we have known winter and malevolent village gossip and ennui, like a marsh in which one gets bogged down, each on one side. Since then, we rendered one another very unhappy. You held your resentment against me so politely that I can't help forgiving *you* for the harm that I did to you.

HÉLÉNE

HÉLÈNE, these phrases are not intended to prevail upon you as a madrigal; it is even passably indifferent to me whether you listen to them; they please me— that is enough.

Do you know, beauty almost equal to a portrait, that as soon as our first encounter, the syllables of your name evoked for me a very white sweetness, a happy slumber on the slow flakes of a calm snow, which would fall for hours and hours, while the little bells of a sleigh tinkled in the far distance . . . Yes, that whiteness, when I close my eyes, breathes the syllables of your name, thus, amid the opiate smoke of Oriental tobacco. And I feel so tranquil.

Afterwards, my head supported on your harmonious breasts, I scrutinize the oddly quasi-Chinese corners of your slightly hooded eyes—and I am then, entirely, the mandarin who philosophizes for himself while waiting for you in a garden planted with unique jonquils, around the great porcelain tower—out there.

Let me search for some soul hiding behind the dark green silk screen on which golden swans are sailing, and which leaves transparent, in its weave, a certain treacherous ember: your eyes. It's singular, my gaze palpates them but I

119

can't penetrate therein. I don't know whether I'm mistaken, but one might think that they were lined with *emptiness*. Tell me, my love, do you, perchance have no soul?

Let us reserve the question, and let me respire the odor of your hair. Oh, what a flower-bed of frail artificial geraniums rises up, which I love for their self-regarding air and their rosy, brazenly modest hue, faintly stained by a suspicion of blood at the birth of every petal—whence disengages now the memory of a rare perfume whose name I have forgotten . . .

I believe, Madame, that you have nibbled my earlobe. I have not, moreover, done you any harm, since you're smiling—oh, but that smile . . . !

By that means, we are reposing on gilded sand in the utmost depths of the vermilion sea; the shadow of steam-ships furrowing the sea descends from above in a dust of ruby sparks, to caress our two heads crowned with delicate seaweed; huge corals rise stiffly on all sides, where many an undine-polyp lies in ambush, thumbing its nose at us.

A warm rutilant sea, your smile; one can easily think of nothing therein!

You're falling asleep? Come into my arms. Very sage, happy to delight in the rainbow reflections that the tremulous flame of the night-light slides over your satiny epidermis, I become torpid in an April twilight—stifled yellows, young blues, dying mauves—lilacs in flower scin-tillate in a light rain that is falling almost soundlessly, in accordance with some frictional rhythm: a slightly sharp wind pinches my nerves agreeably—and as I fall asleep too, amid the wind, the musical rain, and the lilacs, and the April twilight, the white syllables of your name waltz for me alone—Hélène!

AFTERNOON

HOW WARM it is outside! The dog days are weigh-ing upon the city, which is suffocating and fuming in the drunken sun of three o'clock.

Here, one is comfortable; a lowered blind blue-tints the daylight; the room is cool shade and light perfume, in which we are both asleep: the Pauper collapsed, so vaguely, in an armchair; you, O afternoon beauty, naked on the low divan. He admires you—for it is also the sum-mer of your radiant red hair: a star, a ripe crop, a flood of Levantine wine, a fruit of the Hesperides, the crowns on the heads of a queen of fire-spirits (can you count them?) that million tawny gold spangles in which you lie, sure of their attraction and the imminent approach of the kiss.

But why is there such a chagrined expression in his gaze?

"Oh," says the Pauper, "I must confess that I'm an annoying individual. What have I done for you to show me so much forbearance? Since the day I met you, you have loved elsewhere and you have been loved; I loved elsewhere and I was not loved—pretexts sufficient to ex-cuse a caprice, but not a habit. Why were you charming, and I so morose? How does it come about that I am not cured beside you?"

"Bah," she says, bringing him her hair, "what anxiety? Come on, appease your rancor in the hoarse music that is clenched in my voice; breathe in the stormy scent of my kiss and suckle again a little of the crinkled gold of my curls—that consoles . . . And then you'll be cured, eventually."

"No, no!" he cries. "First of all, you're the sun, you're the summer; I venerate the Moon and I'm an autumnal soul. Autumn! You only know it by hearsay. If you knew what mists are within me, in which forests shed their leaves, moaning. In conscience, I ought to flee your beauty, and only admire it from afar . . . but then, judging thus, why always come back to you?"

"It's because you forget to think here," she says; "the dream quits you; it's because such an animal quietude emanates from me that you forget yourself admiring my golds, in caressing, in embracing my nudity without seeking to know whether I have a soul. And then, I love you precisely because of your melancholy."

"But what if I were cured of the Moon; what if I succeeded in strangling my soul to the point of being cheerful, in unison with you, would you love me then?"

"That doesn't concern you. I'm saying that I love you, not that I would love you if . . ."

And like the supple wild panther that she is, she undulates her feet on the carpet.

Truly, thinks the Pauper, that creature envisages things conveniently . . .

Alas, why am I made for the Moon?

THE END OF THE DREAM

I

SILENCE, like an accumulation of cloud on the violet horizon.
Silence, the martyrs in tunics like albs
And a thousand clematis blossoms float in the silence.
Silence, like a very ancient god . . .

A young woman with pale hair and lunar eyes is sitting in the russet grass where orioles are hopping; she smiles strangely, very amused. dispersing swan-feathers in the lactescent air . . .

A spring sleeps, swathed in sweet marjoram . . .

The city, in the distance, is a dragon sheeted in gray and mounted by a knight in an emerald helm.

The sun is so bright and devoid of warmth at the zenith . . .

Bells, great silver lilies, and their clapper a golden pistil, emit scents of benzoin.

A cemetery quivers, strewn with violets . . .

The Prince, leaning his forehead on the knees—so cold—of the young woman—who is death—contemplates an ebony coffin in which a child queen reposes, descending into the depths within himself; but he is bored.

He senses the obsession of a white weeping willow . . .

The Prince gets up; he shields his eyes with his hand and looks toward the Orient, set ablaze by a furious wyvern

A swaying caravan, orange and blue, snakes and tinkles out there, toward a port at which the Mage Kings will embark.

The Prince sets forth and catches up with the caravan. The young woman meditates; one might think that she was praying; the swan-feathers settle.

And the silence darkens . . .

Silence, like an antique carpet, woven with faded figures shiny with wear
Silence, like wings toward elsewhere.

II

The prelude to *Lohengrin* disperses in icy spirals toward the heights. A white daylight reigns, dotted with blue sparks that soar from the tautly-threaded strings of thin harps.

One might think them undulating tresses . . .

A river surges, rolling fire, gold and blood, and draws—with what rapidity!—the funereal gondola that is carrying the Prince.

The Prince says: "That is me, the Pauper of lost roads; that is me, the effigy on forgotten medallions . . . but what does it matter? I am weary of being, and that is why I am taking pleasure, in the leisure of the hour, in stretching my limbs a little on the silky cushion that this gondola offers me; and then too, the landscape is agreeable." And he empties the cup that the Mage-Kings hold out to him.

The banks of the river are fans of coral, from which a red dew falls, drop by drop. Here and there, plaintive madwomen are leaning on the crenellations of towers of jasper. The waves are whispering a melancholy *complainte* as they die away.

One might think that the dwarf Tidogolain is singing his lovesickness in the florid pathways, and that the Lady is moved to pity . . .

The horses of the sun are snorting in the torpid sky: the labarum sun of the Unreal, before which the Prince, suddenly kneeling down, makes the sign of the cross devoutly.

Meanwhile, the faint music congeals in filigrees of ice toward the heights . . .

And the river covers itself with foam, broadly, soundlessly and majestically.

One might think it the slumber of an old man . . .

III

The Night, pale and proud like a royal nun. A river of milk, flowing milk, brushed by flocks of pink flamingos. The slender ivory gondola speeds toward the enormous arches of a marble bridge, where mutilated knights, in armor corroded by rust, are leaning over the cool rumor of the waves.

Low in the sky, a half-moon, cherry red and violet.
And the Night seems a cloister in which golden nuns are kneeling.

The Prince extends himself in the bottom of the gondola, facing the stars. "Such soft velvet ramps this Night for the ascension, with groping hands, of my blind soul! An infancy within me is astonished by so much shadow and charitable gold; I sense new eyes blossoming within me, better to reflect the poppies and periwinkles in flower up there . . .

"Oh, I would like a little of this Night to enter into my heart!"

The gondola passes under the bridge; an antique thunder awakens; dusty flags are waved; bats circle.

The knights cry: "Take us with you; we were in your retinue when, quitting the Unfortunate Isles where you reigned, you attempted the conquest of the Princess of Pearls . . ."

The Prince sings: "*The knights are dead in the crusade . . .*"

Then they all throw their shields into the river.

But the gondola has passed by.

IV

Let's disembark! Let's disembark! The air is vibrant with the wings of delight; the verdure bursts forth cruelly; a swell of flowers undulates, swollen with good sap; a red vapor trepidates in the distance; and the Summer bounds like a young tiger through the countryside.

It is the harvest, the harvest of poppies.

"What red intoxication rises to our brains here? My Prince, you are tottering, and your hands are clenched."

"Oh! Look, here comes the jubilee with the redness of dreams. Oh! look at all that red, resounding with triumphal marches . . ."

The poppies are crowded together, in rubescent expectation; the poppies are strutting, heavy and somber; the poppies are swollen, an infernal paradise, a sunlit debauchery of red slumber. And long arrows of fire hail down on the exultant earth; terrible perfumes, as impetuous as stallions, sonorous perfumes, like red trumpets of conflagration.

It is the harvest, the harvest of poppies.

Large golden insects with ruby stripes and adamantine wings circle and dispute their opiate juices, and then fly away to deposit their booty in crystal hives dazzling in the distance, on the edge of a tawny wood.

The Prince rolls over among the poppies: streaming blood, and imperial couch, a crimson cloak of pensive dreams, a glory of orgy and oblivion that drowns him with furious kisses.

And the Prince falls asleep. Red petals bleed over his lips; red opium lees tint his fingernails; red sweat glistens on his forehead of a Christ of Illusion haloed by the irritated swarm of golden insects.

It is the harvest, the harvest of poppies.

V

Beneath the starry night, the exceedingly somber road snakes across a plain, yesterday's battlefield, covered in corpses. Wounded horses, abandoned, whinny dolorously; the winter wind stings the wounds that shine in the dark, like the flowers of aloes. The dead sleep, quite tranquil, with the astonished expression of no longer being alive; their eyes congealed by horror reflect the stars.

All alone—his Argonauts have remained, inebriated, in the poppies—the Prince marches with a long stride, toward where? He does not know; he goes on. Sometimes, rarely, people whom he encounters salute him and fix him with long, sad gazes. Judging by the wrinkles that slash their faces, one suspects that they have suffered a great deal; none are limping. Some whisper to one another, reflect, and then come to the Prince as if they want to give him some advice, but they stop, and back away. *What's the point?* they seem to be thinking. And they pass on, after having bowed very low, not without a certain irony.

The Prince also stops, and turns round; he thinks, confusedly, that perhaps he would have made them some reply if they had spoken, but what? He has forgotten. And he passes on.

Silence, like attentive eyes.

Meanwhile, a rumor is born at the extremity of the horizon; fleeting lightning flashes puncture the night, setting the countryside ablaze for the time of a thought, and then disappear.

And the Prince arrives on the seashore.

VI

The rotating beam of a solitary lighthouse is radiating its desert light in swarming prisms over the waves, as far as the eye can see. The sea crumples its seething waves at the foot of the lighthouse, where enormous white cetaceans

spout phosphorescent geysers. A fringe of foliage blood-
ies the ashen horizon faintly, which closes on the traveled
route close by. Night closes its golden lashes.

The Prince climbs up inside the lighthouse; an iron
staircase rings under his footsteps; at the summit, in the
multicolored cage, there are three watchmen in mourning. The Prince goes to speak to them, but with fingers
over their lips they enjoin him to be silent. Then they
draw him toward a window open over the sea and point
into the distance, where a blue radiance is visible . . .

There—O unknown Dream!—somber fir-forests are
moaning, undulating; fields of broom are ringing a million little golden bells in the wind. A roseate marmoreal
palace rises up; on the threshold, an old man . . .

The three watchmen precipitate the Prince into space.

VII

Riding a blue ray of light on which Ariel is dancing, the
Prince flies, at lightning speed, into the distance. The
theme of the Holy Grail trembles in the darkness, and
Astolfo's hippogriff circles.

Sudden daylight: the warm light of a summer day;
pale mists like a drizzle espoused by the morning. And
the sea becomes exasperated, and brandishes algal standards toward the nacreous cliffs.

O familiar Dream: it is the Island.

The Prince follows the florid meandering paths—all
legend acclaims him—and arrives before the palace, so
pink in the somber enlacements of ivy. On the perron,

an exceedingly old King is waiting for him, among the twelve peers of Dream and dainty illusory fays; and buccinas of gold and bronze roar, frightening flocks of doves, feathered snow among the firs. The King descends a few steps to meet the Prince; he takes him in his arms and kisses him on the mouth.

"My son, you have suffered life and the dream; you were the Pauper of the lost roads and your feet are still bleeding because of the pebbles that lacerated them during your pilgrimages in the land of Consciousness. Listen: your ordeals are over, you have donned the alb-like tunic of silence; your recompense is due. Come, the slumber with no tomorrow is open to you; your soul will breathe in Nothingness. Come and sleep with us, my son."

VIII

Misty Thule sways on the waves, like the flower of the lotus in which the three gods meditate. And so many essences of unusual souls—the Prince and the Pauper, the King and his twelve peers, the genteel fays; all of legend—repose forever, delighted, in the Afterlife.

Silence hangs over Misty Thule.

Silence, like a virgin, with lunar eyes,
*   dispersing swan-feathers in the pale air.*
Silence, like a cemetery strewn with violets,
silence, like our mother: Death.

THE PAUPER'S PHILOSOPHY

My melancholy is attached
to the essence of things.
SHAKESPEARE, *As You Like It.*[1]

---

1 This back-translated line does not appear in the English version of
the play, but French translations of Shakespeare are often very free.
The sentiment expressed is a drastic contraction of Jacques' speech
on the subject of melancholy in Act IV Scene 1.

A LONE, in this room where there were joys, elbows leaning on the table cluttered with many unfinished manuscripts, which will yellow as such under the dust of forgetfulness, the Pauper is dreaming.

It is night, no longer the newborn dream cradled far from things, no longer the great Charity of innocent gazes, but a bitter stepmother whose surly hands hurl handfuls of December rain against the window-panes. Deformed Life presides, and its ironic laughter; and the surrounding city ululates in accordance with the ruddy fog and the winter.

However, the Pauper is dreaming.

"For a long time I have lived, the plaything of appearances, in a garden of sensuality where, in order to feast my eyes, crimson violence and the golden incitement of an entire flora of mad perfumes vibrated, amid the murmur of water that sings and fleeing like a siren. The demon of the Flesh came there and kissed me on the mouth; no fever remained to me of its kiss. A fresh spring awoke in me, which endowed the flowers of the garden with the eternal infancy of flowers—beautiful and dangerous, like the voices of women—for my soul had the name Insouciance.

"One evening I encountered the obsession; the garden faded irrevocably.

"With what delight I welcomed that Idea! Crowned with the ivy that dissipates the fumes of Drunkenness, it was the young Muse modulating on a light flute the harmonious counsels of Wisdom. I loved it for itself alone: close at hand, in the attitudes of an ignorant goddess, or distant, floating in the golden vapors of a dusk of ancient ages; and I dedicated a temple to it in which I inclined by ecstasies at the feet of its silence. There, my soul had a name, its Religion.

"'Idea,' I often begged, 'goddess Idea, are you the truth?' Then I sought a certainty in her eyes, which seemed impassively retreated toward anterior eurhythmics. When she deigned to respond, it was thus: 'I am the Truth because I am the knowledge of yourself. Knowing yourself, you will acquire universal consciousness, because the apparent world is only a reflection of the interior world; the Spirit moves the spheres and the Spirit is within you. Be solitary and know your soul.'

"Bitter doctrine, as dazzling and as cold as crystal! However, I accepted meekly the labor prescribed, and for many days, I strove toward my most intimate Being. Leaning over the tenebrous well of my soul, I noted the vague echoes that the modulations of the magic flute awoke therein; I listened to the wind of Abstraction engulfing therein and agitating, in vague phosphorescences, the rhapsodic black water of my thoughts; my passions were only the pebble that one drops in order to calculate the depth of the well . . .

"Desolate labor, sterile labor, from which I am still shivering!

"When, finally, weary of so much vain effort, I looked around, the elect temple fell in ruins, and the Muse faded away in indecisive mists. I felt very old, and the mocking conviction rose up of having been deceived. Then my soul had the name Desert.

"'Oh,' I cried, 'life exists and I am hungry for its embrace. I shall find elsewhere what I could not discover in my Being!' The world was promising, scintillating and musical; the world was the Idea with a thousand facets, which it was necessary for me to study one after another; I set forth on the research of life.

"Renewed adolescence: obscure bells in the depths predicted future Grails."

※

"I think I am arriving—I arrive. It is the charming and evil Isle, Misty Thule, where I am lost. The Idea lived there, according to some redoubtable avatar . . .

"Now, she was not the icy Goddess who floats at the zenith of the soul in soft moonlight, soothing the raucous and gentle wrath of a lascivious sea, on the threshold of a marmoreal palace, the most deceptive of the daughters of Hecate. Her smile was the sensuality sovereign over herself and the other, her eyes the black double star that signifies misfortune. For myself, I only believed her smile, and that she was the Idea.

"Oh, from then on, in her arms, death of time and space, forgetfulness in her bed, the luminous poison of her kisses leaving a taste of blood on my lips.

"The Island, for us, was rhythmed by poems of gorse, enervated jasmines and cadences of moaning firs; impalpable wings quivered, in undulating aureoles, in the lukewarm fog of a languid late summer afternoon; the savage Ocean sang the epithalamium of the wedding of the Dream and my soul. What did the Norms—Solitude, Abstraction, Penitence—matter to me henceforth? I read my thoughts in the eyes of the daughter of the Moon; my ecstasies were toward her gestures; I drank all science in the charm of her speech, in which the harmony of the worlds resonated; she reigned, the Isis whose veil I had lifted! And through her, my soul had the name Joy."

"One day, skimming the waves, she left, going toward some puerile chevalier, helmed in gold and haloed by the dawn, who had appeared on the western horizon. And when they were far away, I fled, forsaken and bleeding, cursing the Isle and the Idea.

"I landed in tumultuous cities and fairground music. I wandered, insane, seeking to kill my soul, striving to rain all cups, with the hope that it would finally discover the desired toxin therein; I encountered Circe, who offered me her nepenthe; I picked and trod ferociously the barbaric multicolored grapes of debauchery in order to extract therefrom the black alcohol of a grim dream, with which I impregnated my Being; I was a wicked Christ, agonizing in an infernal Passion . . . Everywhere, always, I rediscovered the Idea, daughter of the dreaming Moon, surging forth from the deceptive labyrinths of appearance; and I no longer had any but this happiness: a memory of a smile illuminating some of the turnings of drunkenness. In order to cure myself of that I sought any amour whatsoever: arms that were held out, pitifully, which I rejected; others, vile, in which I lingered with delight—the smile remained victorious . . . And the bitterness of nothingness persisted within me because of so many fruits bitten and then rejected . . . Finally, often, very often, I returned to Circe; her nepenthe drove away *the smile*; I drank it to the lees.

"It was then, through the intermediary of a reverie as immense and as vague as God, that I wrote pages in which my distress sang and howled—these pages (of which this is the last): a year of life.

"And my soul had the name Madness."

The Pauper wanders around the room. Dolorous and very vague, his gaze settles on once-familiar objects. What sullen indifference their aspect brings forth! Do they not seem to say: "From months and months, you disdained us; we have forgotten you, as you have forgotten us. Today, if you want to recover, include in us, the little of yourself that you once confided to us, you need to want new gazes."

"Oh," the Pauper replies, "the malefic lamp is extinct; I am no longer the assassin of my soul: the strange Pauper who lived that deadly year has gone away . . .

"But so many proofs, suffered in the adverse ways, even when wounds that were slow to heal persisted, give me the right to forgive myself. I can see again! I foresee the unknown gleam that will enlighten me as to the good Idea. The other face of life is beginning to appear, and its mystery is welcoming. The golden swarm of healthy thoughts is already buzzing, and wants to escape toward the royal flora of the primal gardens of Insouciance. I want to be, again, the man with the eyes of April, which attract, amid the laughter of light lilacs, under the mildness of a yellow sun, the iridescent dance of rhythms. Soon I shall have recovered the necessary innocence; everything will be an unexpected marvel to me; a radiant Dream will guide me, via paths of music and perfumes, far from hollow metaphysics and passions that kill, toward the Mont Salvat of the truth. And my soul will have the name Childhood.

"As for you, fervent somber pages, glimmers of a defunct nightmare, which will not be resuscitated, return to the Devil, your father—I will never read you again."

The December tempest has fallen silent. A blue morning descends from the sky and sows diamonds over the city. The room is soft and warm in which the Pauper, the cheerful Pauper of old, is busy with his zigzag writings, sketched poems, and whistling, rejoicing in the claustral atmosphere, the dancing fire and its thousand little multicolored wyverns. And he savors the reconquered benevolent aspect of familiar objects.

"Bah!" he says, laughing at himself. "It is written—logically, moreover—that 'Everything finishes in songs.' So, a few verses will close miraculously, by way of an epitaph, this veridical, albeit bizarre, book as well as they commenced it . . . And then, rhythm and rhyme and all Poetic Art is still the best thing there is in life, unless it's sleeping, or killing time doing nothing . . ."

EPILOGUE

I

*O*NCE, *cares undulated in the plaints of oboes.*
Velvets! and such sobbing—viridian laughter that
                                                  [*unfurls—*
A triumph for an Isis adorably thin
Glory of a blue-tinted park where turtle-doves coo.

Toward the strange vibrant azure birds mad on whiteness.
Toward the cloud, fateful shadow and giant's gesture
    Hunting in a vain tumult of hours,
Isis, once a goddess, you are going pale, and your heart
Is a park of withered lilies and bleeding poppies.

What a year! Is that magic over, then?
What winter, all winter, is darkening your brow?
Here comes life without wings and gray reason:
My eyes are weary; it's the end of the comedy!

Like one who is leaning over my soul I see there
    Dislocated tartans sinking

And a thousand standards of old
    Becoming frayed in faded water;
    Like one who lures the future,
Like one who dreads tomorrow's dawn, I remember
The blue gardens of doing sweet nothing and sleeping
    Where Chimeras spat gold
    Into the clotted blood of porphyry . . .
"As for our Isis, yesterday's queen, she'll have to be buried!"

    "Shut up, leave that dust in peace;
    It's the Past, I tell you, the Past:
    Don't be the man that a shadow exasperates—
And if your soul is old, if your soul trails and wants to forget:
Here's smiling Circe with her opiate philter."
"Oh, drink . . . flee once again into the crimson of an auroral
                                      [dream—
But no: it's a long time that I've been dead."

II

Plucking the mad grapes from equivocal trellises,
I have savored the golden inferno of fresh pulps;
From the accursed espaliers where vermilion fruits are
I have collected sin like a fine peach.

    Everything escapes me that was charming
Even—like a Night baited with bright stars—
The Beauty whose eyes were my only flowers
    And her song of a lunar bird—
    Everything deceptive intoxicated me yesterday.

However, O unreal fanfares,
Today is the feast of the fraternal angels
On the luminous parvises of tomorrow's palaces
Where, to crown me King of the perennial Dream
The stars in the sky are falling to kiss my hands.

Today, I know what my dementia was;
My soul of old is sleeping in its tomb.
And rich in infinity and clad in innocence,
I am going, like a child, along new roads.

(Paris, October 1889 — Tours, January 1891.)

A PARTIAL LIST OF SNUGGLY BOOKS

LÉON BLOY *The Tarantulas' Parlor and Other Unkind Tales*
S. HENRY BERTHOUD *Misanthropic Tales*
FÉLICIEN CHAMPSAUR *The Latin Orgy*
FÉLICIEN CHAMPSAUR *The Emerald Princess and Other Decadent Fantasies*
BRENDAN CONNELL *Metrophilias*
QUENTIN S. CRISP *Blue on Blue*
LADY DILKE *The Outcast Spirit and Other Stories*
BERIT ELLINGSEN *Vessel and Solsvart*
EDMOND AND JULES DE GONCOURT *Manette Salomon*
RHYS HUGHES *Cloud Farming in Wales*
JUSTIN ISIS *Divorce Procedures for the Hairdressers of a Metallic and Inconstant Goddess*
VICTOR JOLY *The Unknown Collaborator and Other Legendary Tales*
BERNARD LAZARE *The Mirror of Legends*
JEAN LORRAIN *Masks in the Tapestry*
JEAN LORRAIN *Nightmares of an Ether-Drinker*
JEAN LORRAIN *The Soul-Drinker and Other Decadent Fantasies*
ARTHUR MACHEN *Ornaments in Jade*
CAMILLE MAUCLAIR *The Frail Soul and Other Stories*
CATULLE MENDÈS *Bluebirds*
LUIS DE MIRANDA *Who Killed the Poet?*
OCTAVE MIRBEAU *The Death of Balzac*
CHARLES MORICE *Babels, Balloons and Innocent Eyes*
DAMIAN MURPHY *Daughters of Apostasy*
KRISTINE ONG MUSLIM *Butterfly Dream*
YARROW PAISLEY *Mendicant City*
URSULA PFLUG *Down From*
JEAN RICHEPIN *The Bull-Man and the Grasshopper*
DAVID RIX *A Suite in Four Windows*
FREDERICK ROLFE *An Ossuary of the North Lagoon and Other Stories*
JASON ROLFE *An Archive of Human Nonsense*
BRIAN STABLEFORD *Spirits of the Vasty Deep*
BRIAN STABLEFORD (editor) *Decadence and Symbolism: A Showcase Anthology*
JANE DE LA VAUDÈRE *The Demi-Sexes and The Androgynes*
JANE DE LA VAUDÈRE *The Double Star and Other Occult Fantasies*
RENÉE VIVIEN AND HÉLÈNE DE ZUYLEN DE NYEVELT *Faustina and Other Stories*